This book belongs to:

ABC
Letter Tracing
FOR
Preschoolers

The Letter A

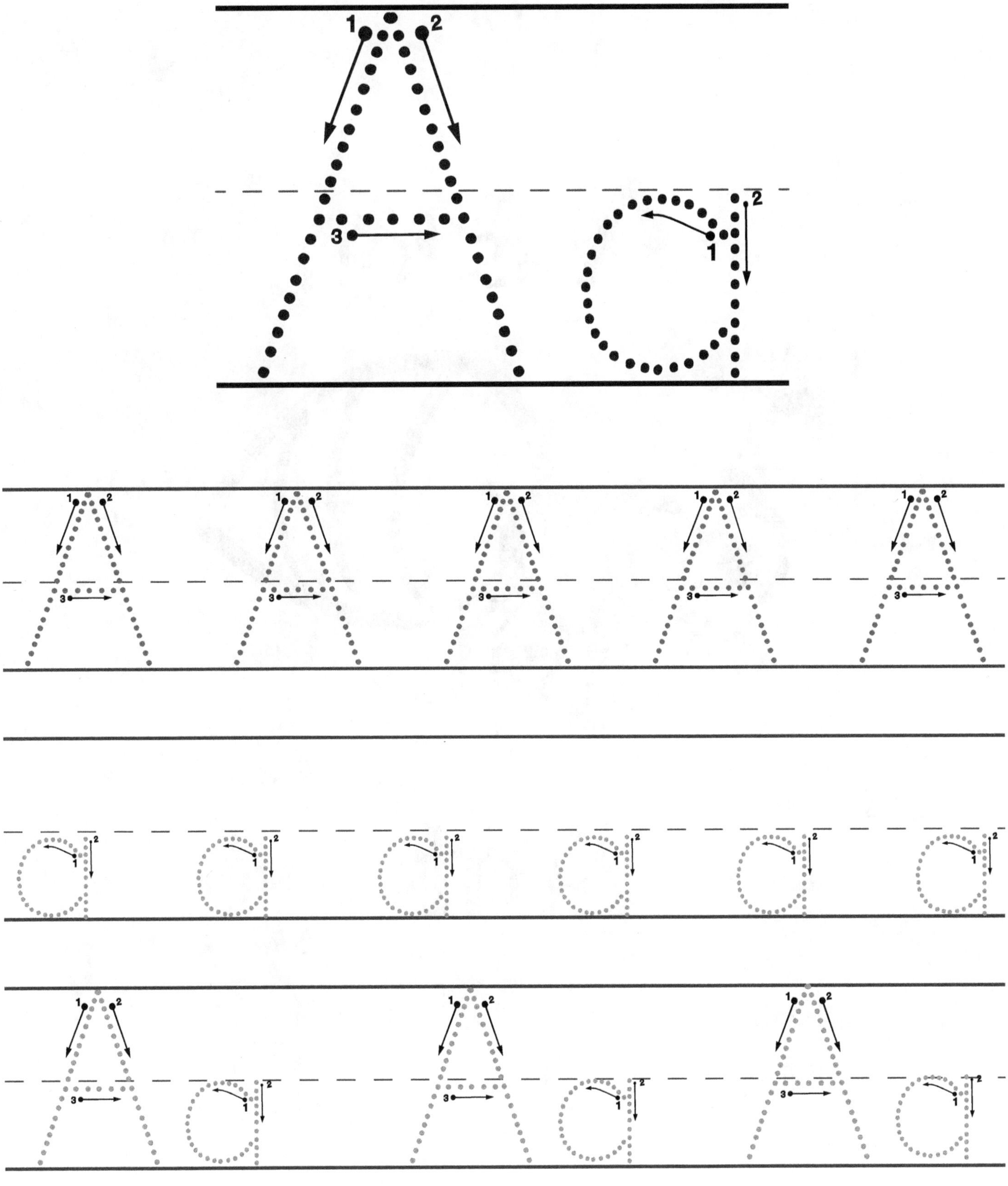

A is for

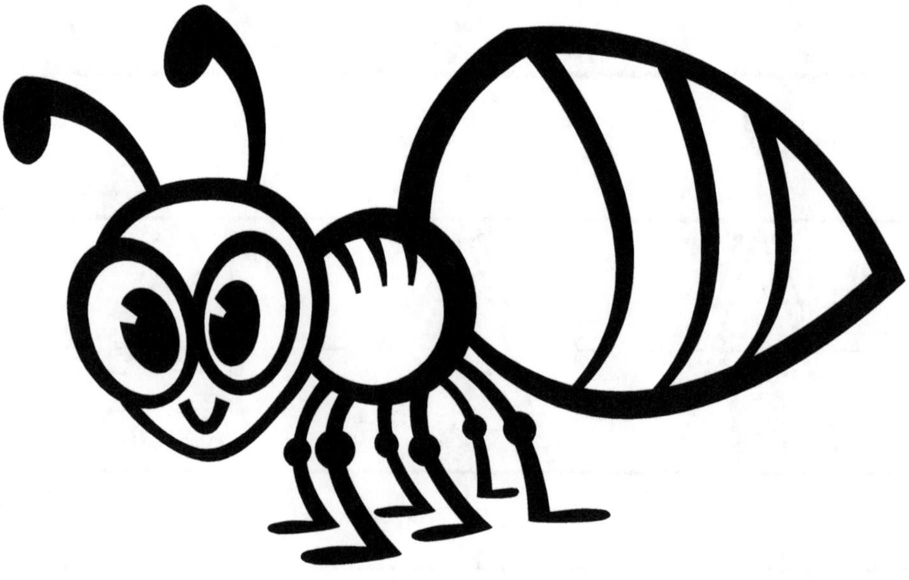

Ant

A

A A A A

A A A A A

A A A A A

A A A A A

A A A A A

A A A A A

a a a a a a a

a a a a a a a

a a a a a a a

a a a a a a a

a a a a a a a

a a a a a a a

The Letter B

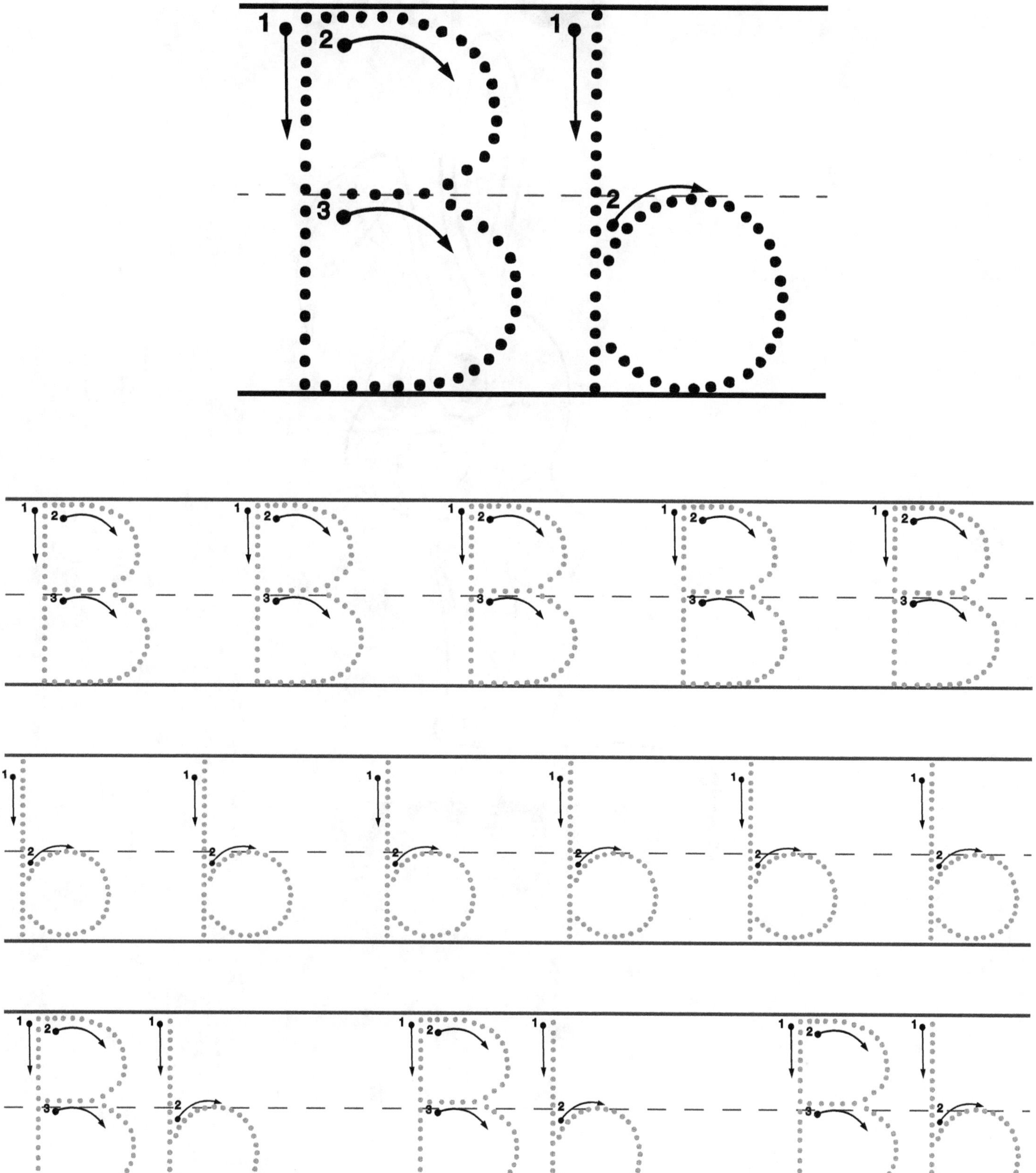

B is for

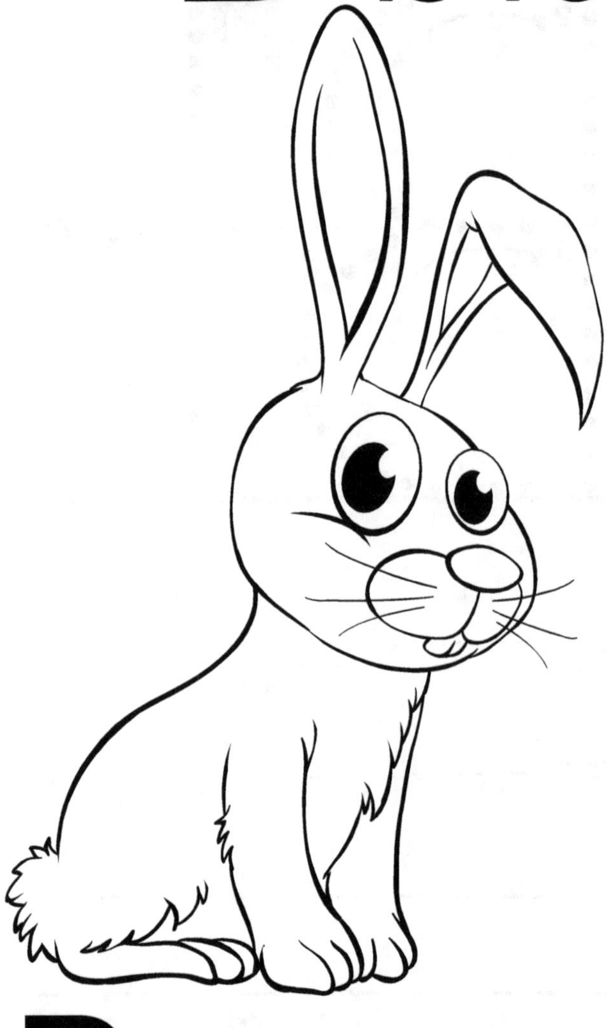

Bunny

B B B B B B

B B B B B B

B B B B B B

B B B B B B

B B B B B B

B B B B B B

b

The Letter C

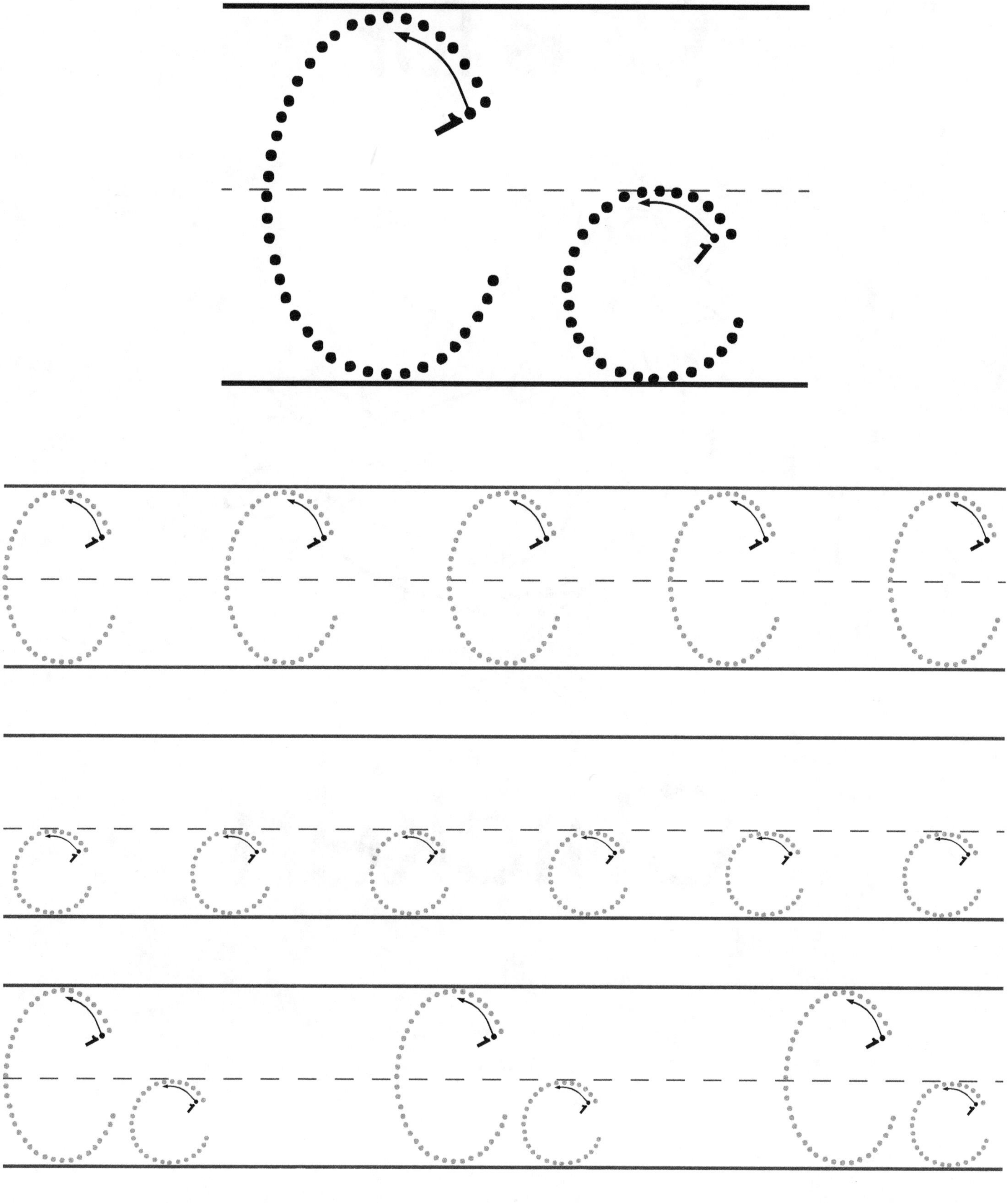

C is for

Chicken

C

C C C C C

C C C C C C

C C C C C C

C C C C C C

C C C C C C

C C C C C C

c c c c c c c

c c c c c c c

c c c c c c c

c c c c c c c

c c c c c c c

c c c c c c c

The Letter D

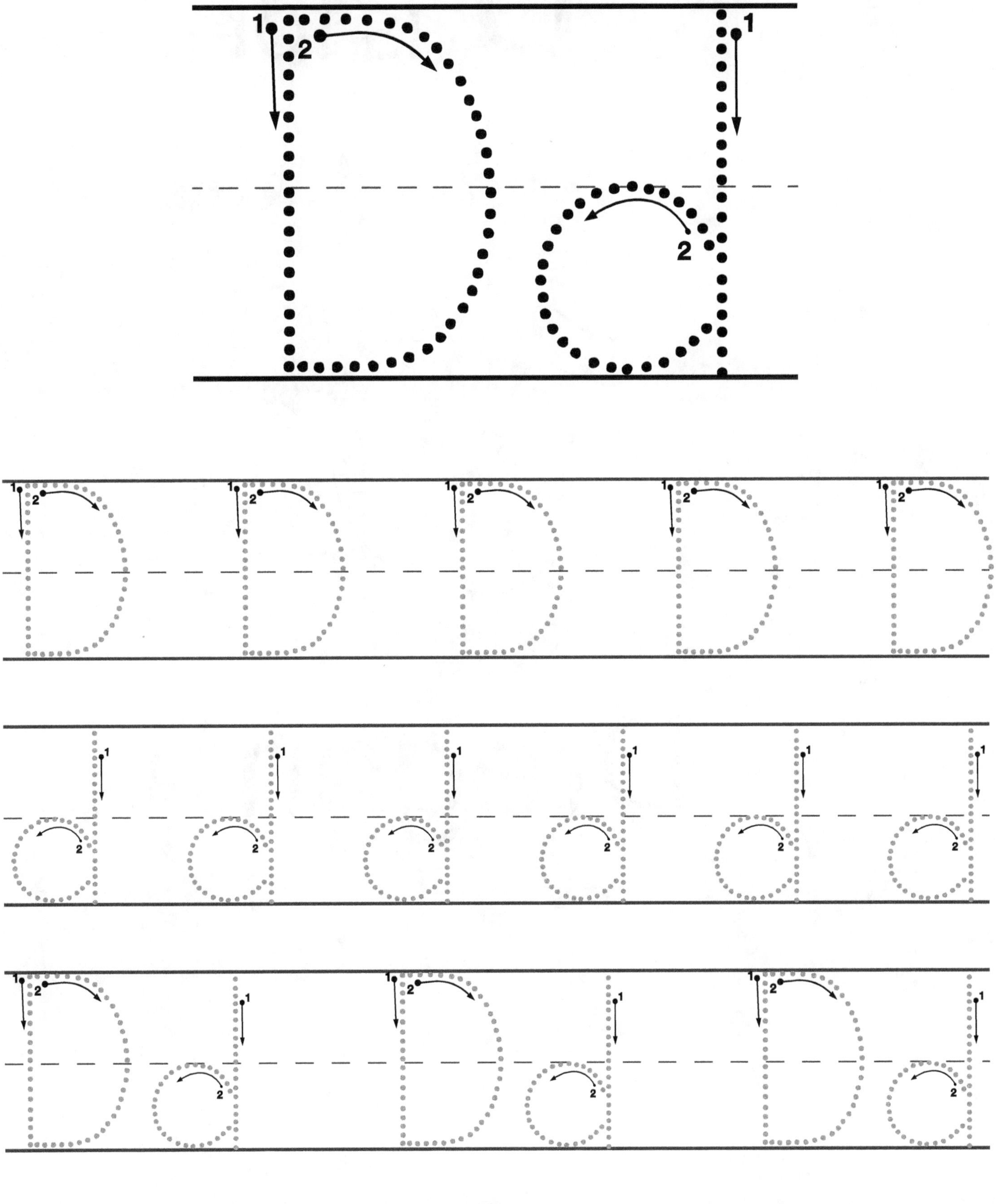

D is for

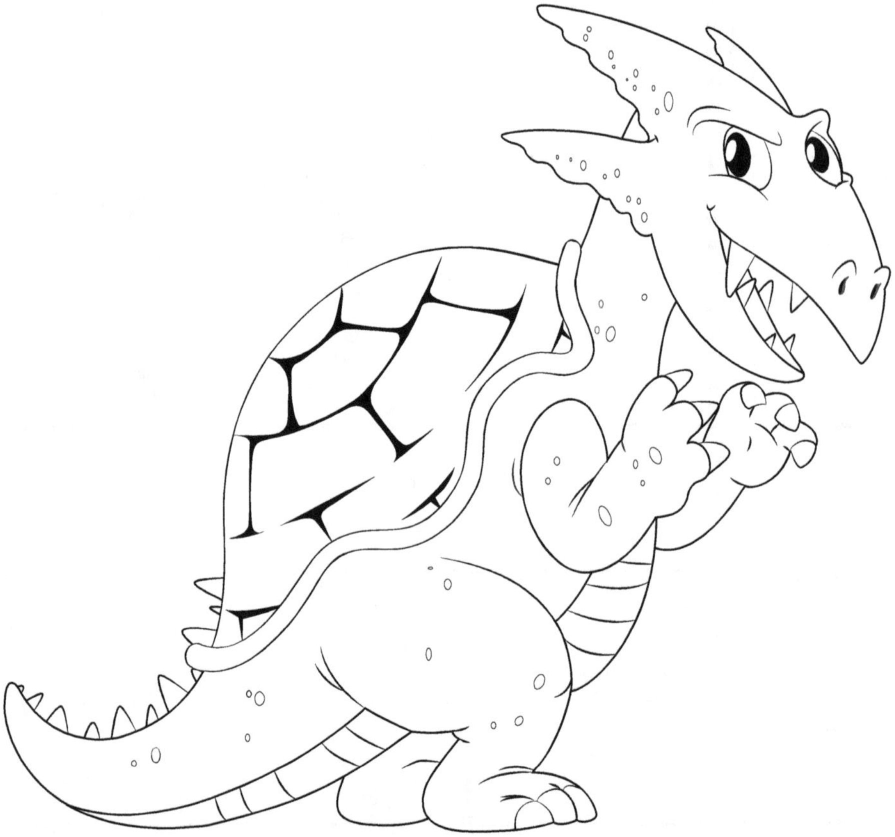

Dragon

D

1 2

d

The Letter E

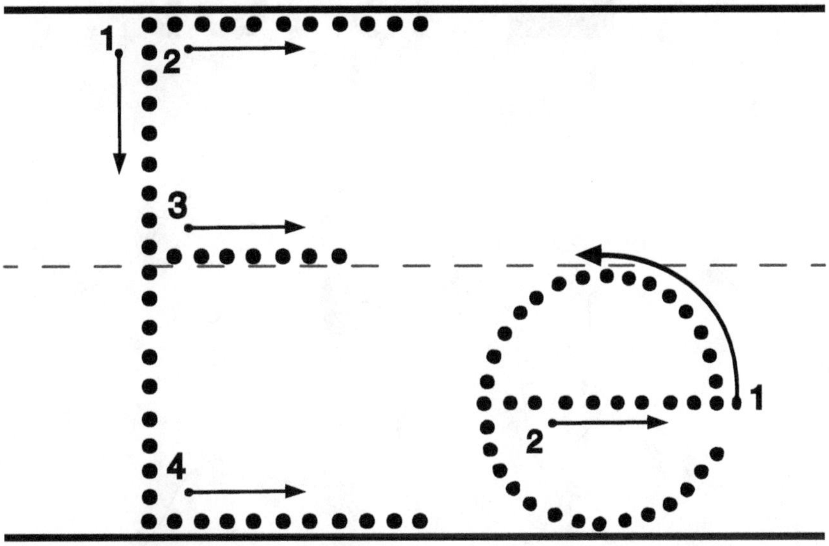

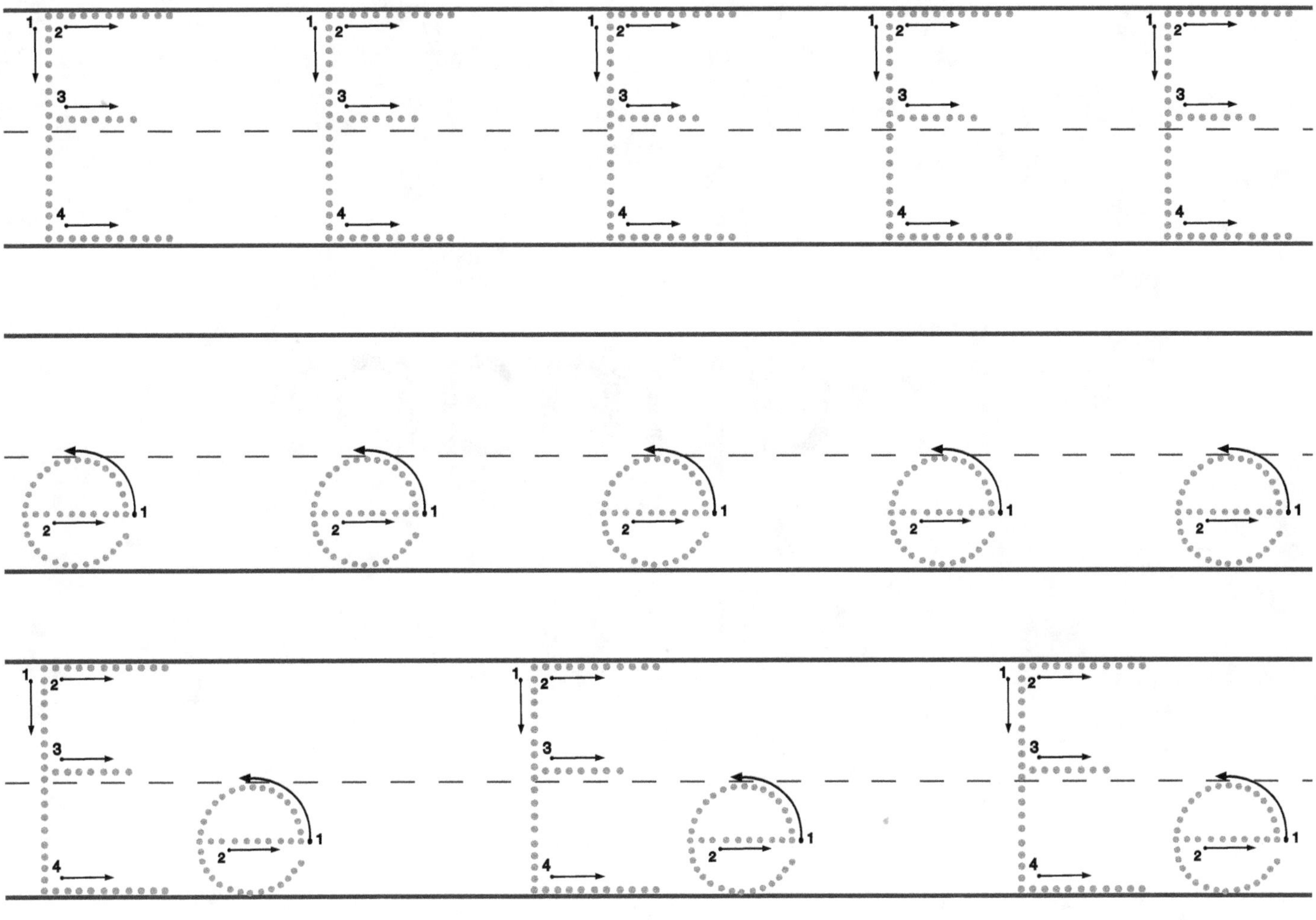

E is for

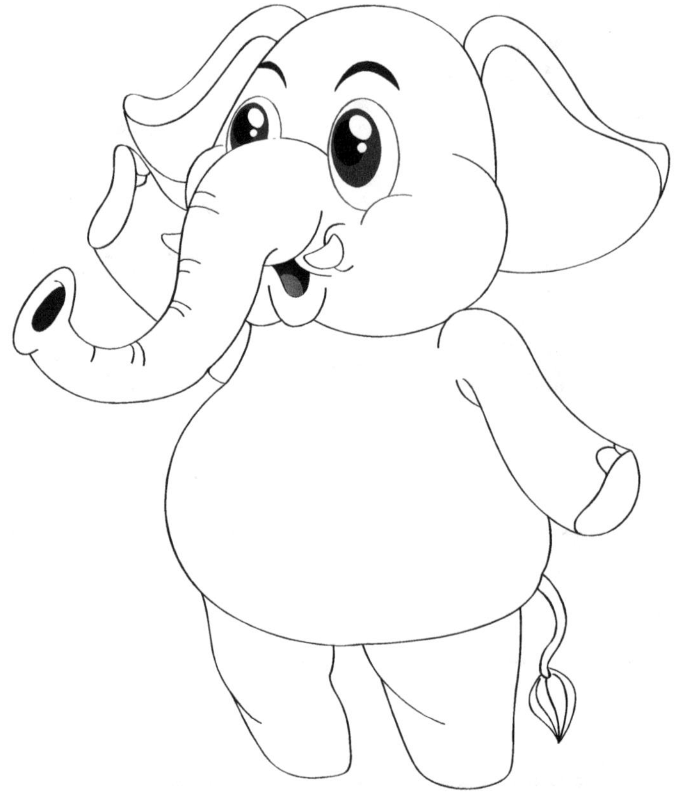

Elephant

E

1 2 3 4

e

The Letter F

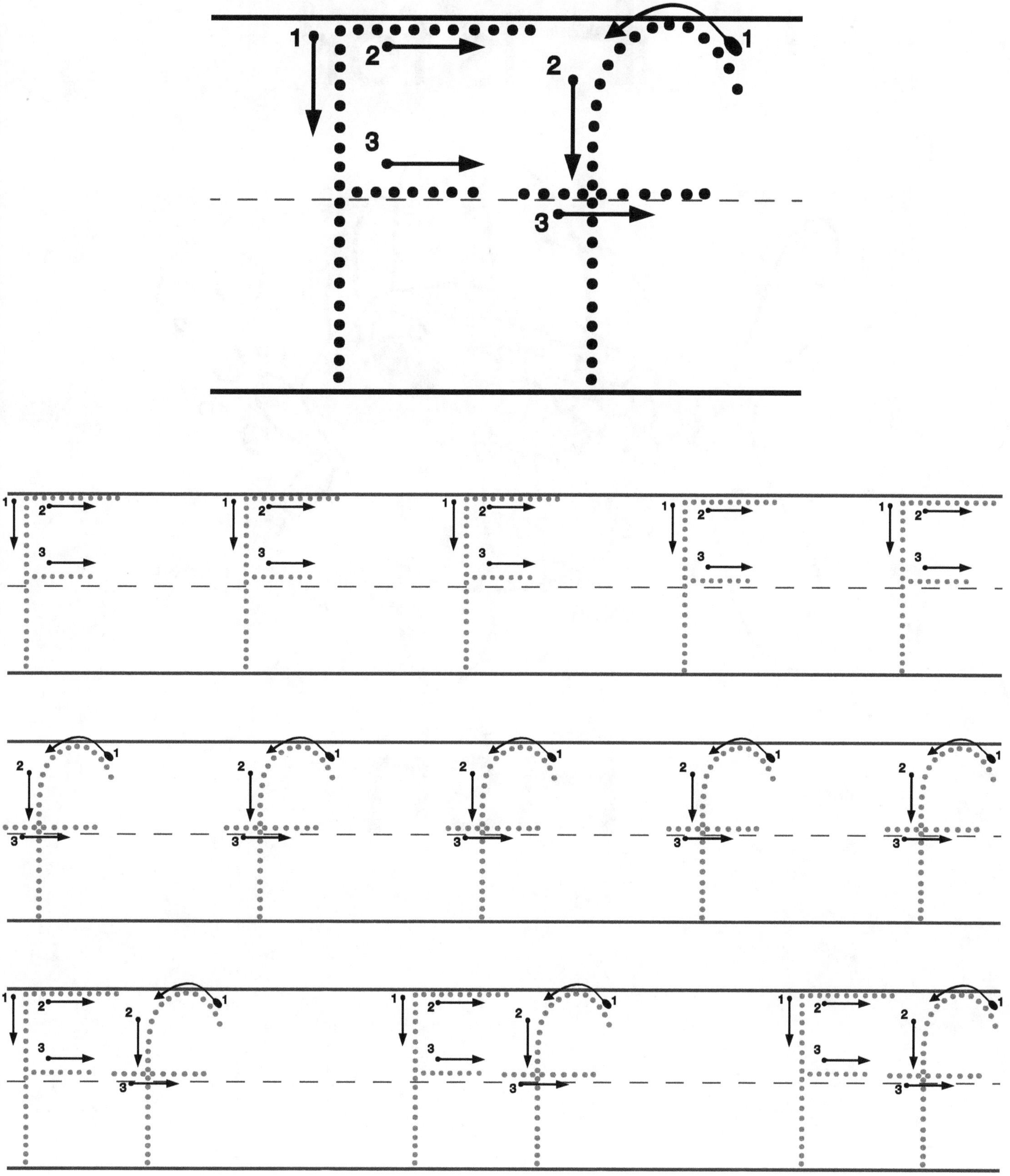

F is for

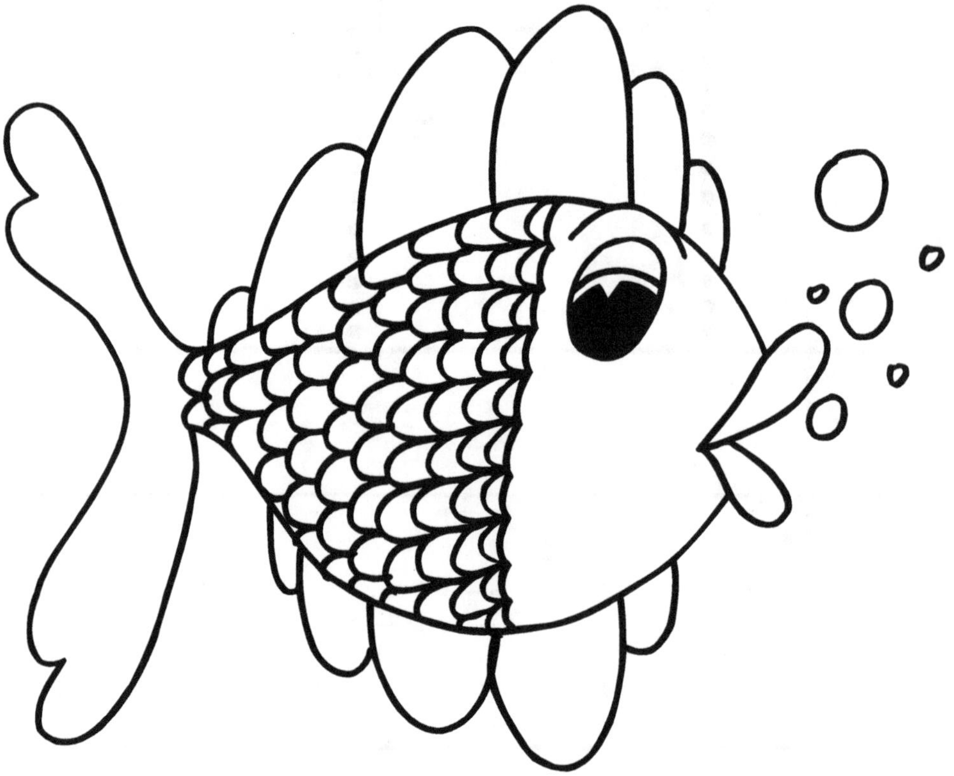

Fish

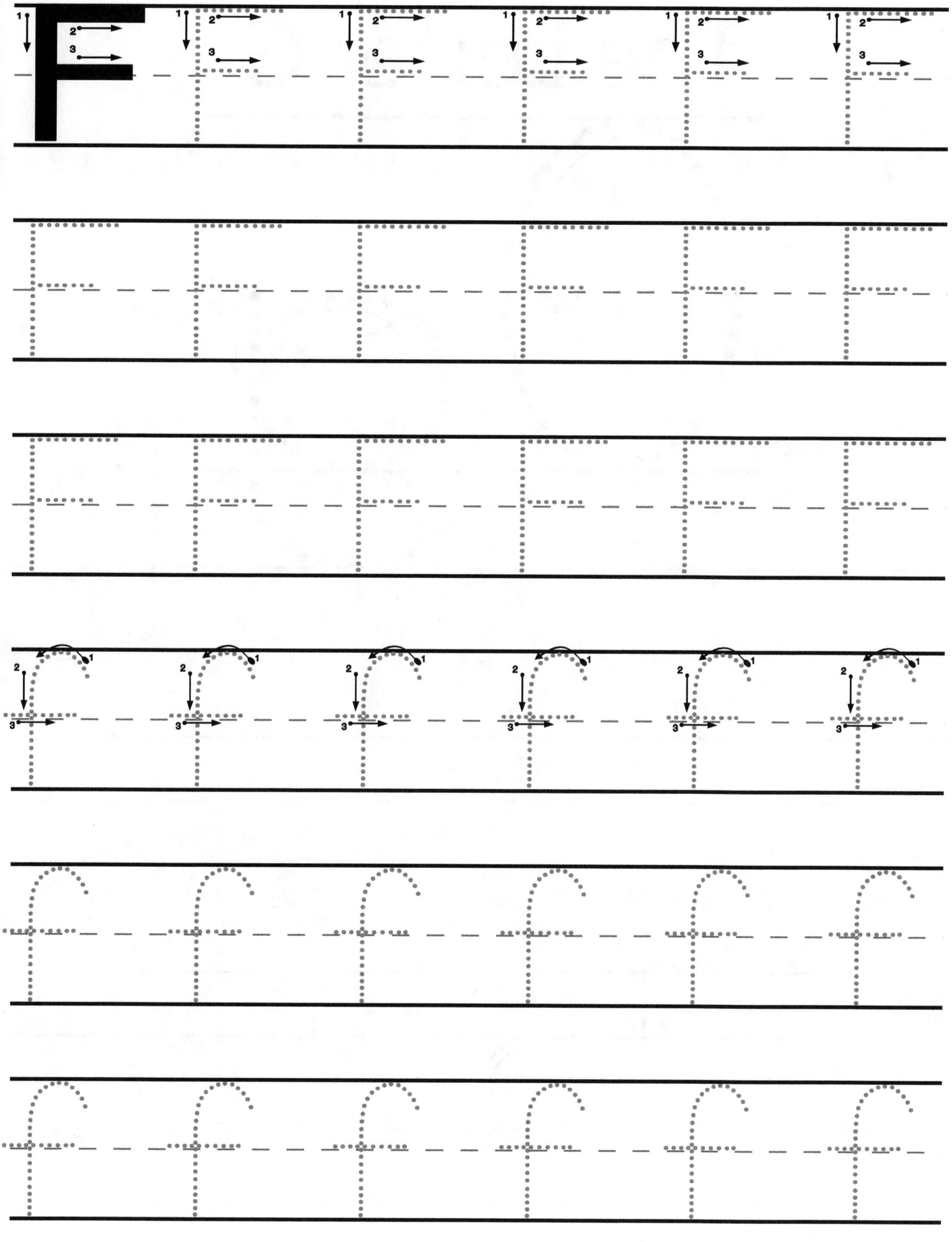
F

The Letter G

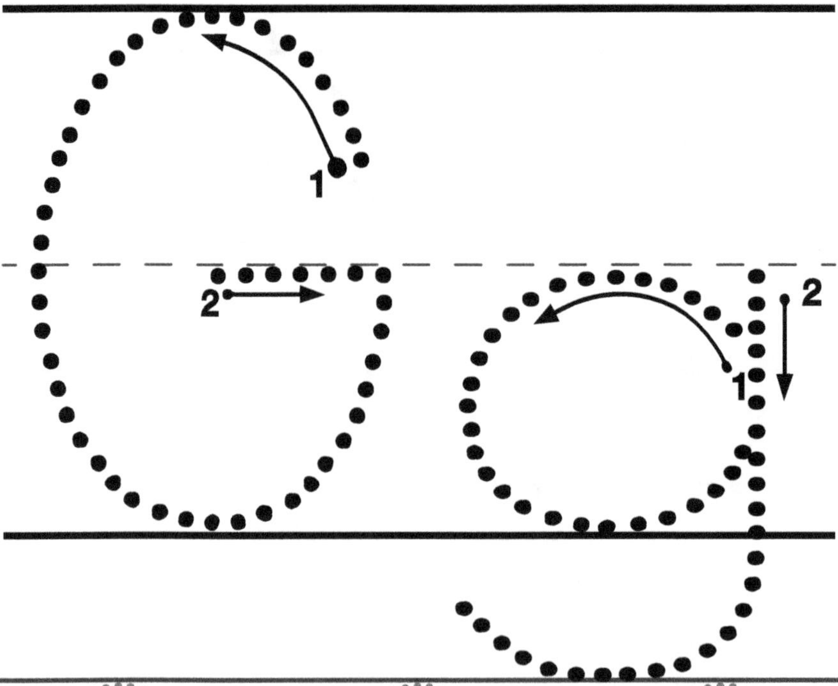

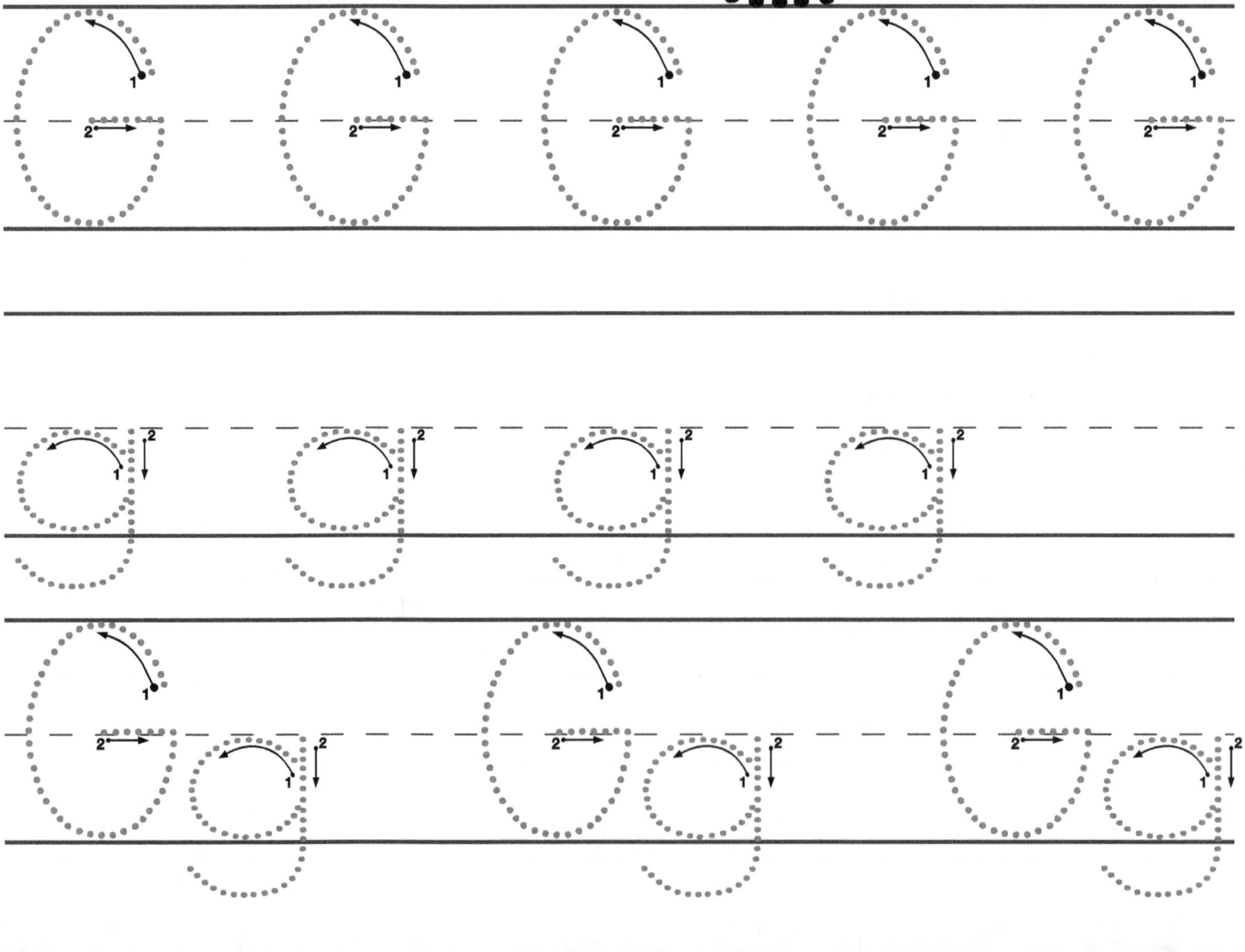

G is for

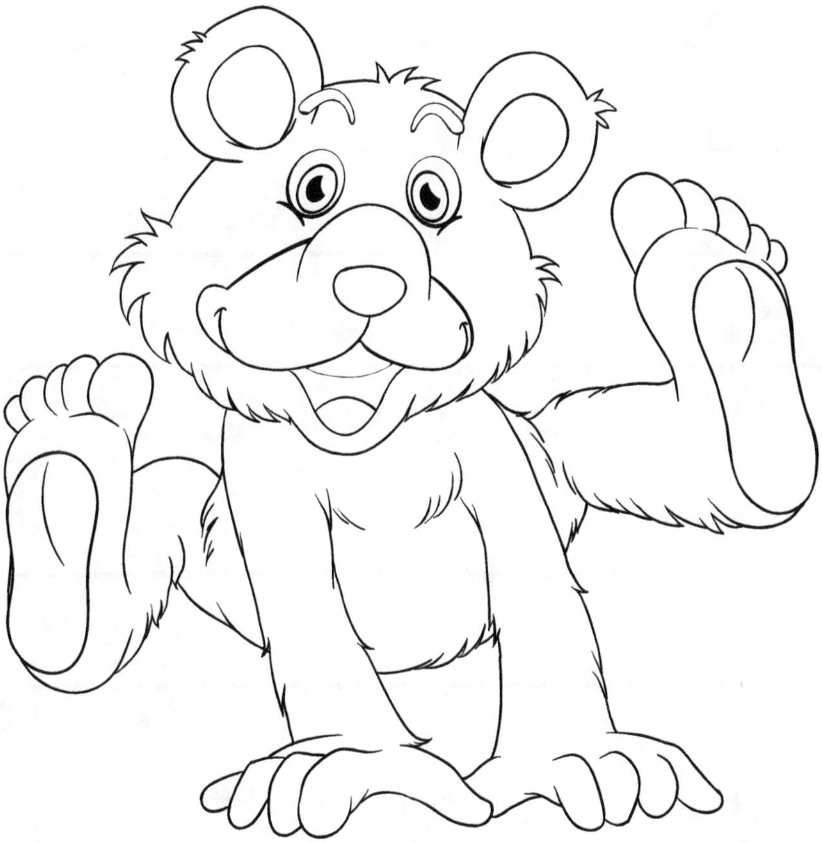

grizzly bear

G G G G G G

G G G G G G

G G G G G G

g g g g g g

g g g g g g

g g g g g g

The Letter H

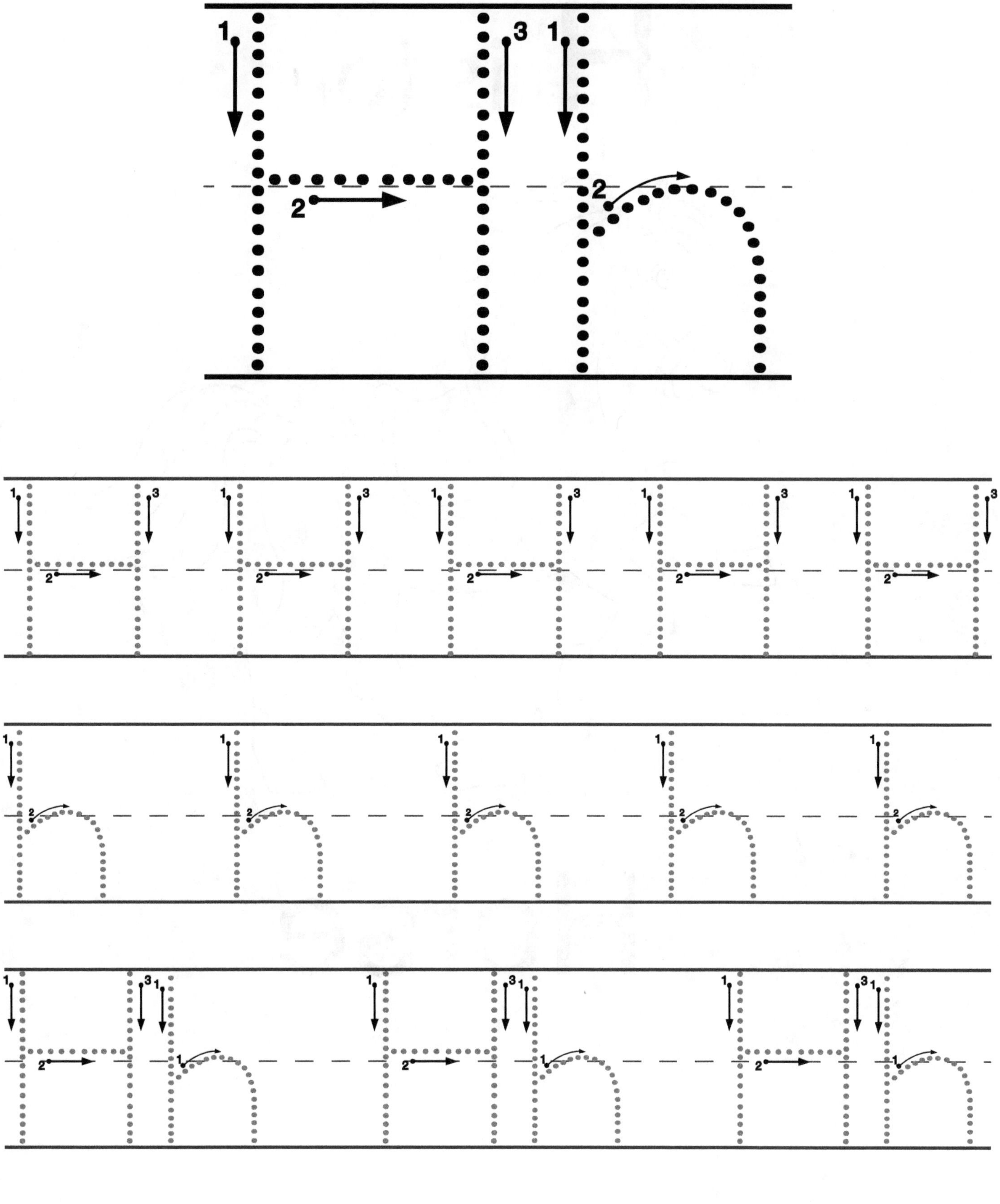

H is for

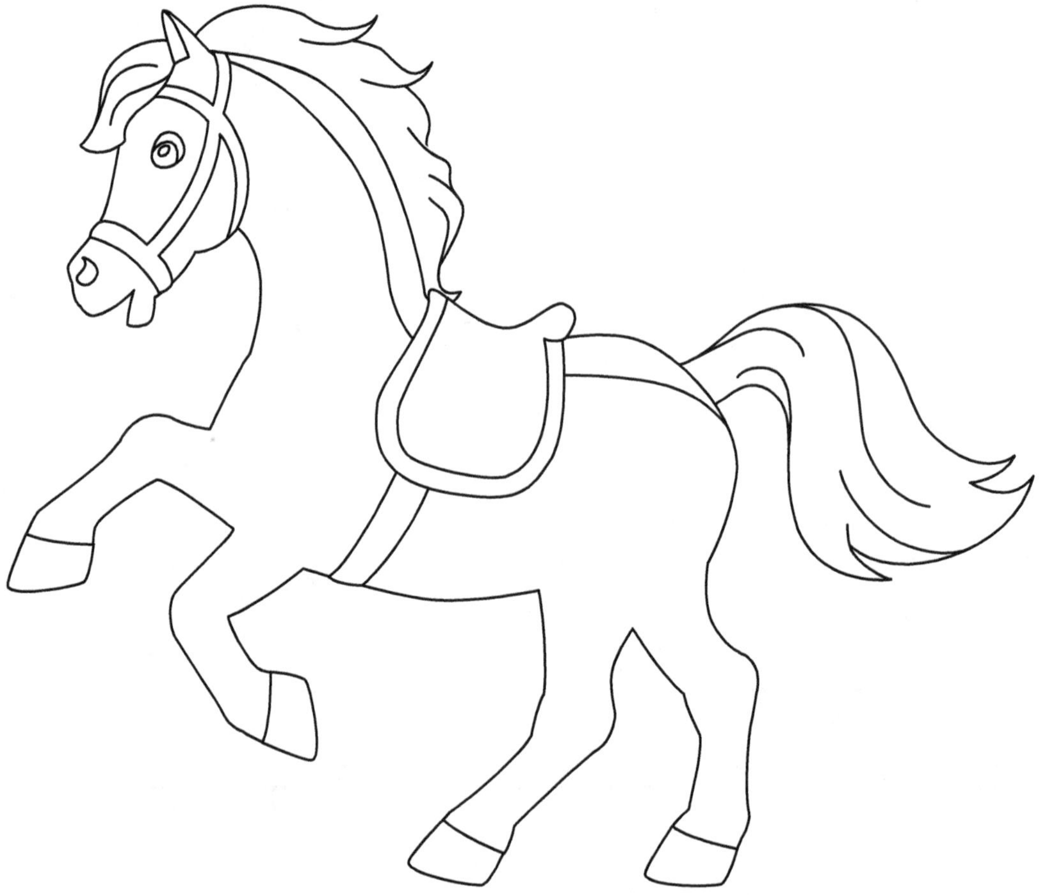

Horse

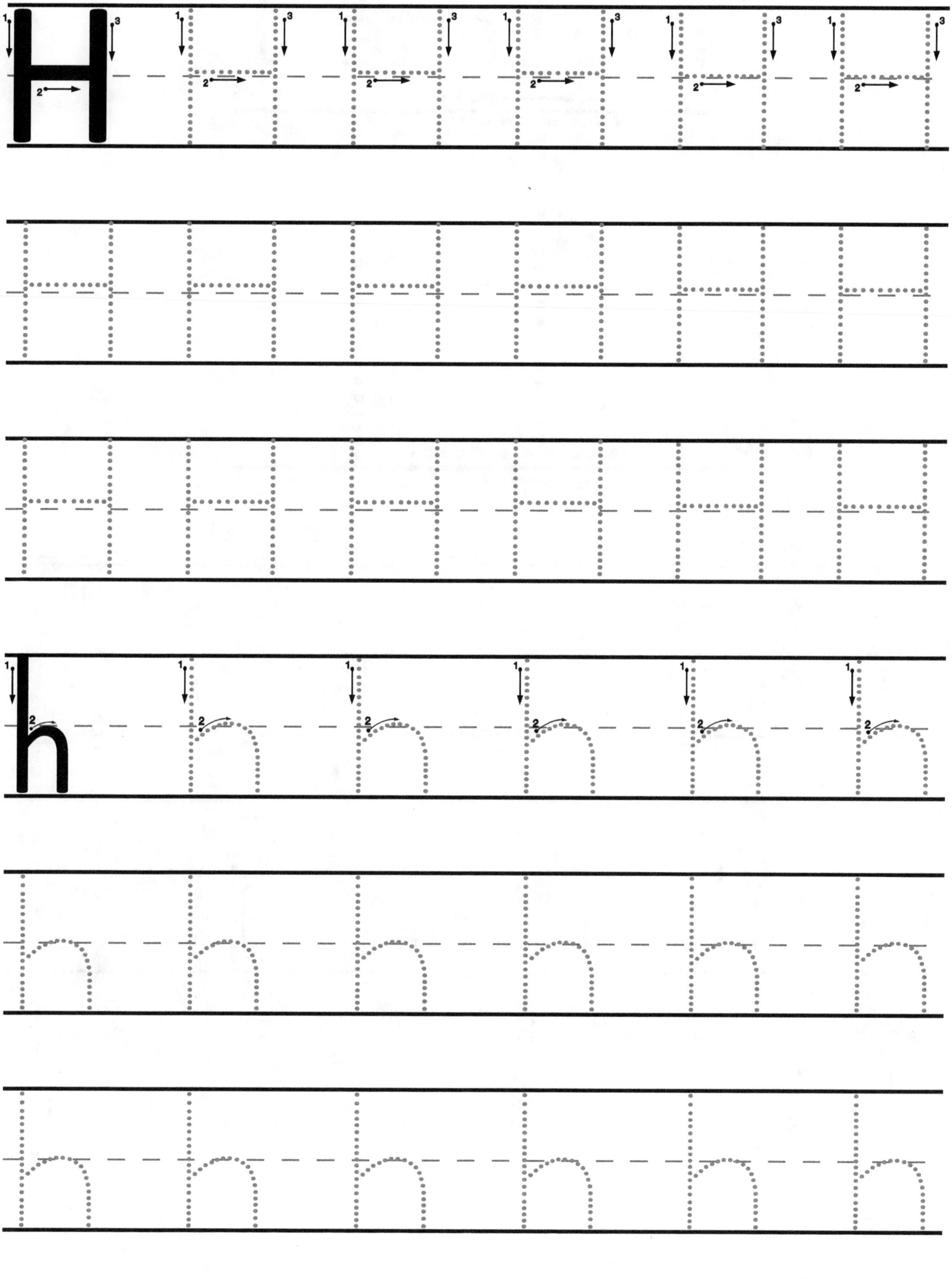
H
h

The Letter I

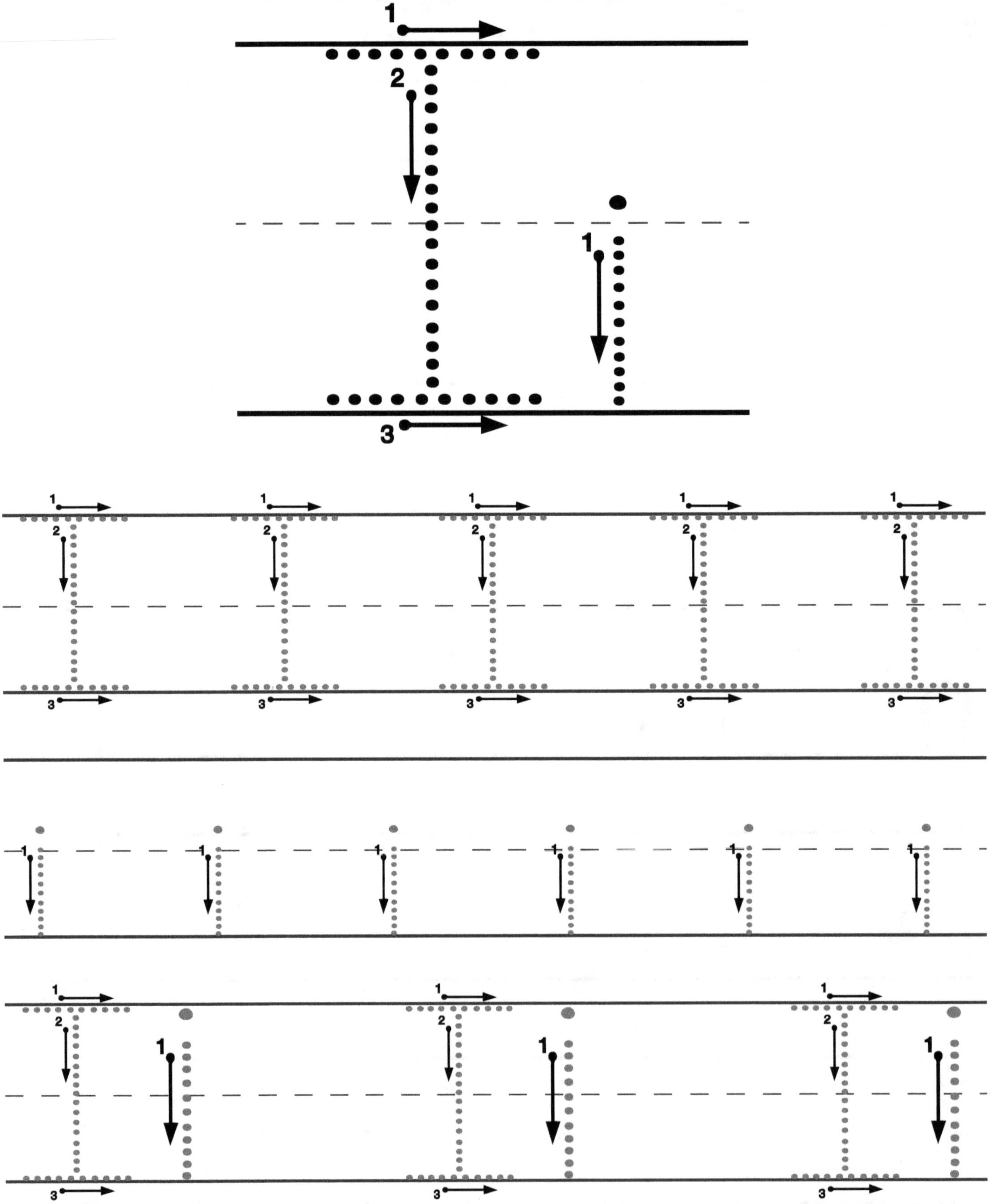

I is for

Impala

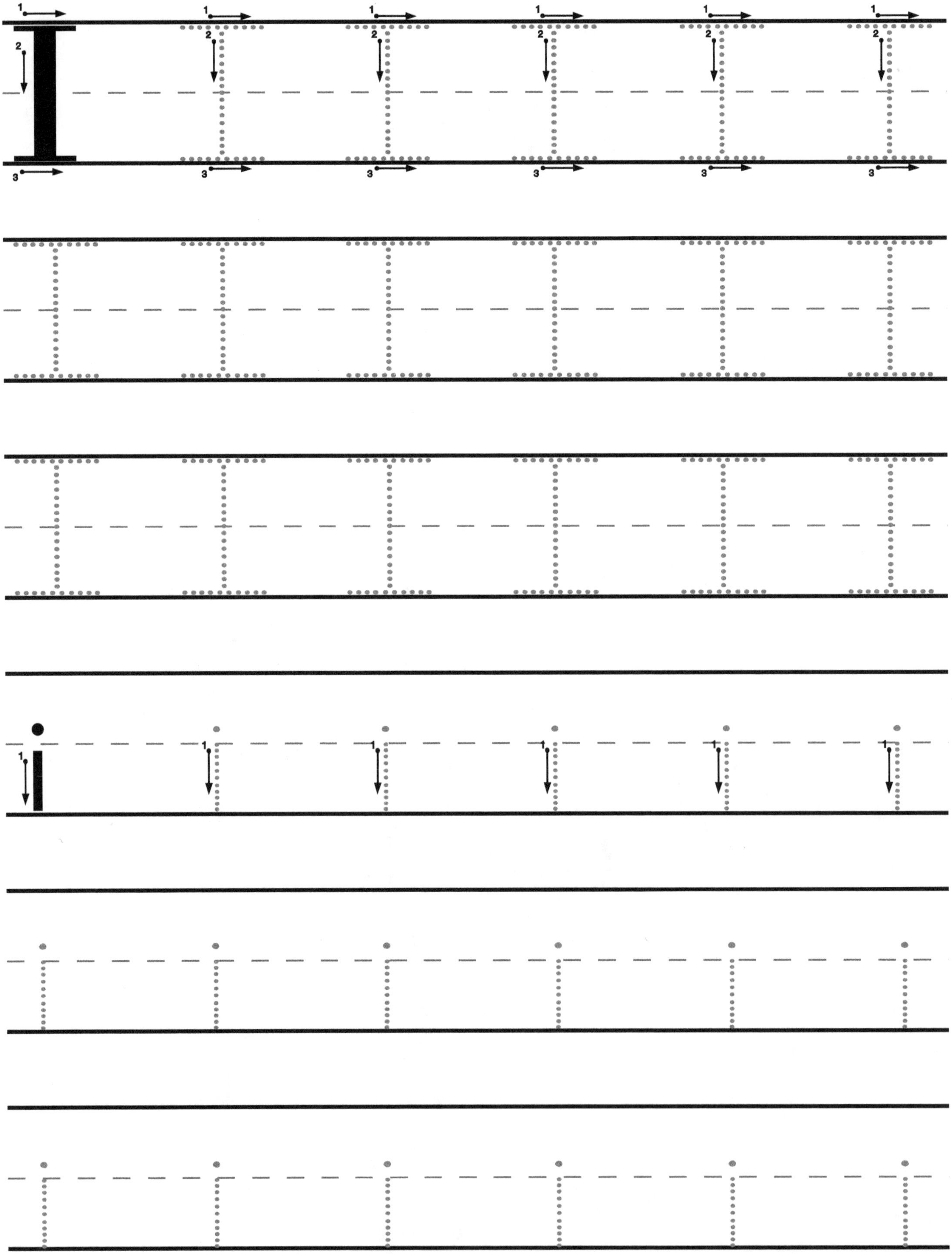
I
i

The Letter J

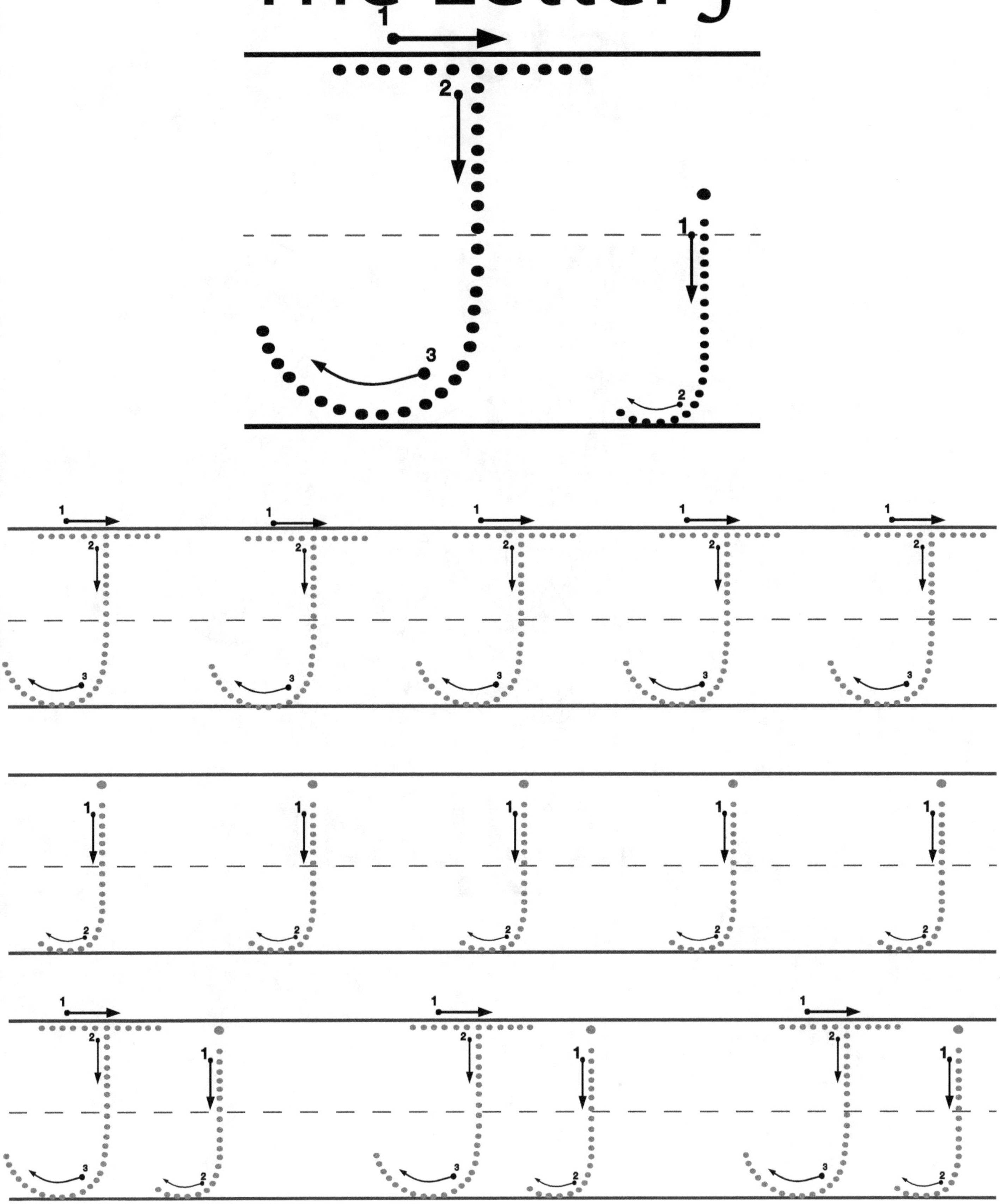

J is for

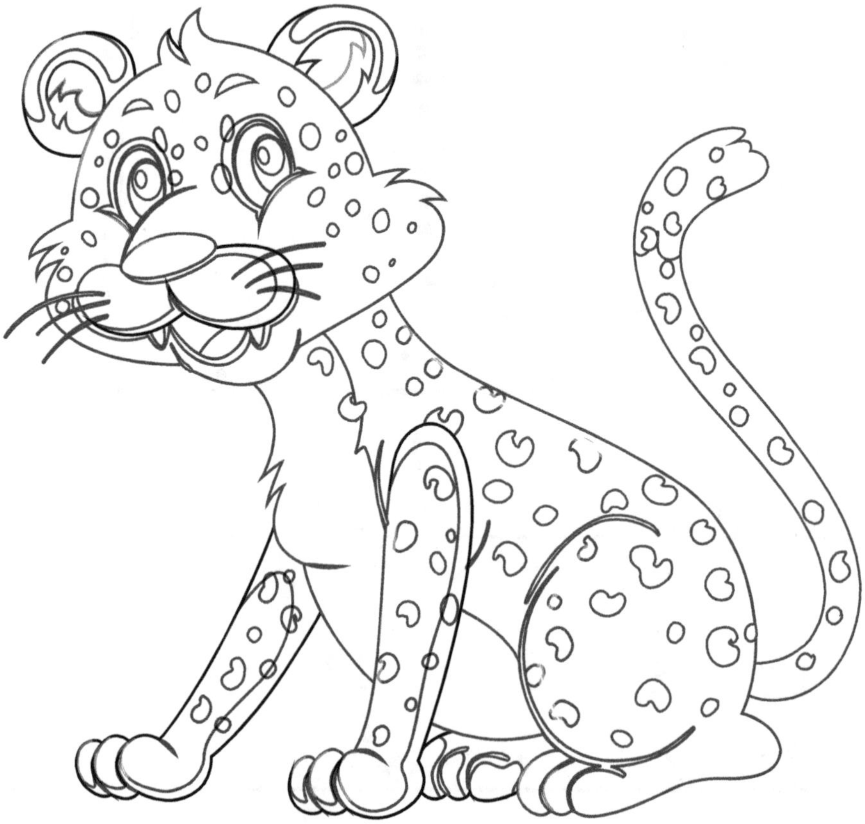

jaguar

J

j

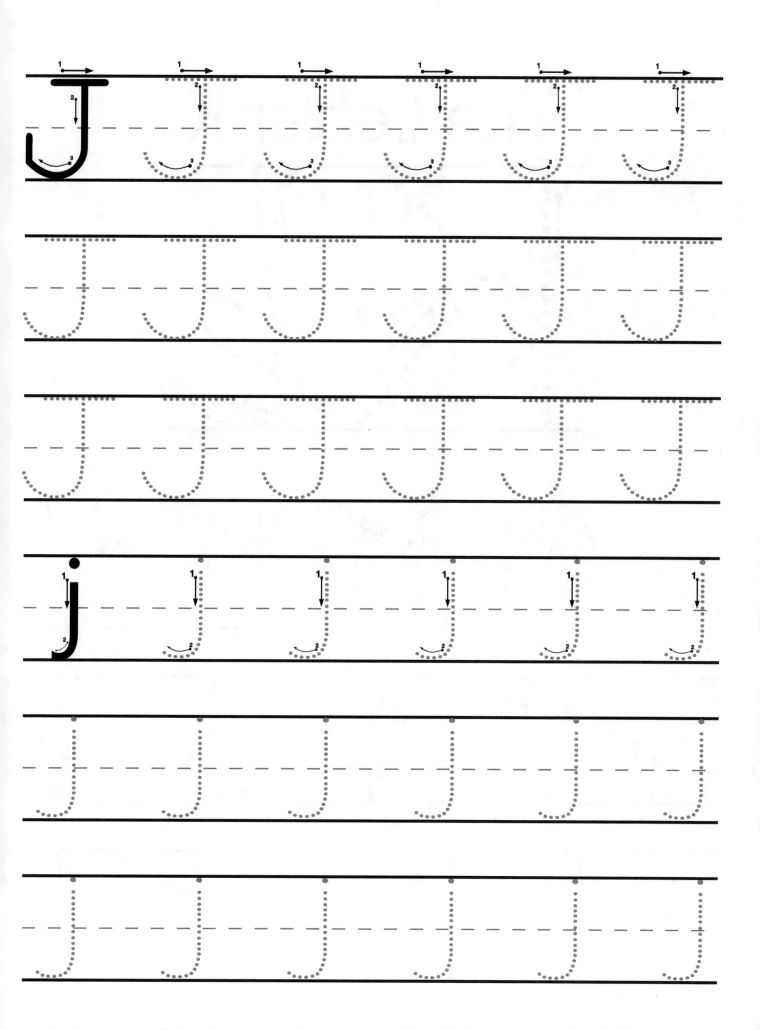

The Letter K

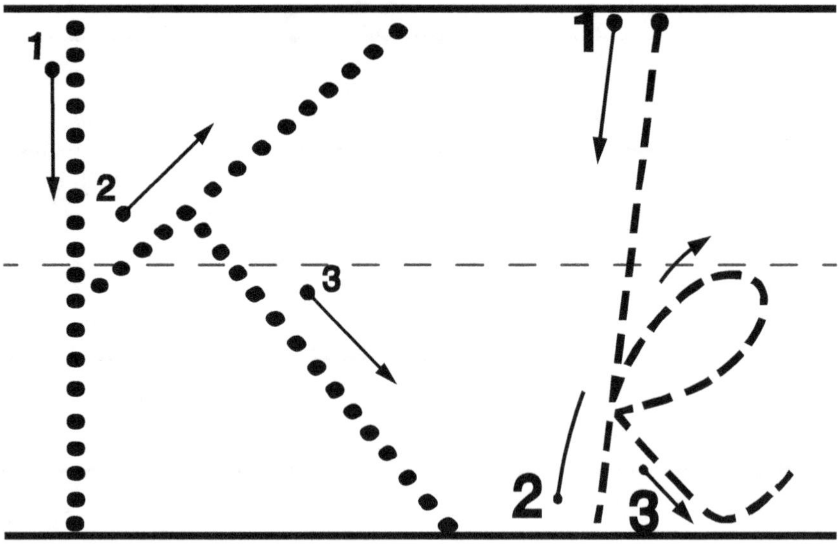

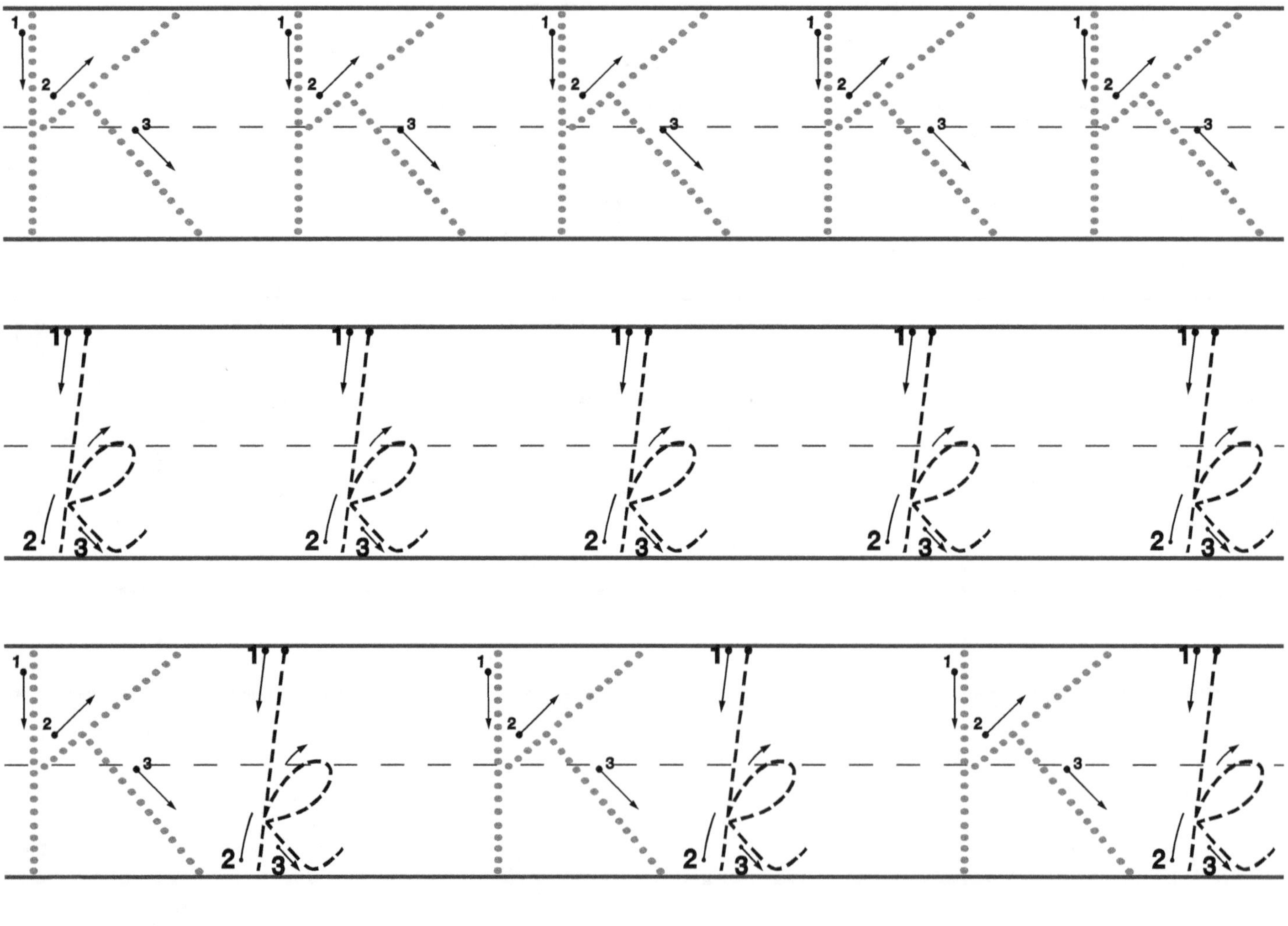

K is for

kangaroo

K K K K K K

K K K K K K

K K K K K K

k k k k k k

k k k k k k

k k k k k k

The Letter L

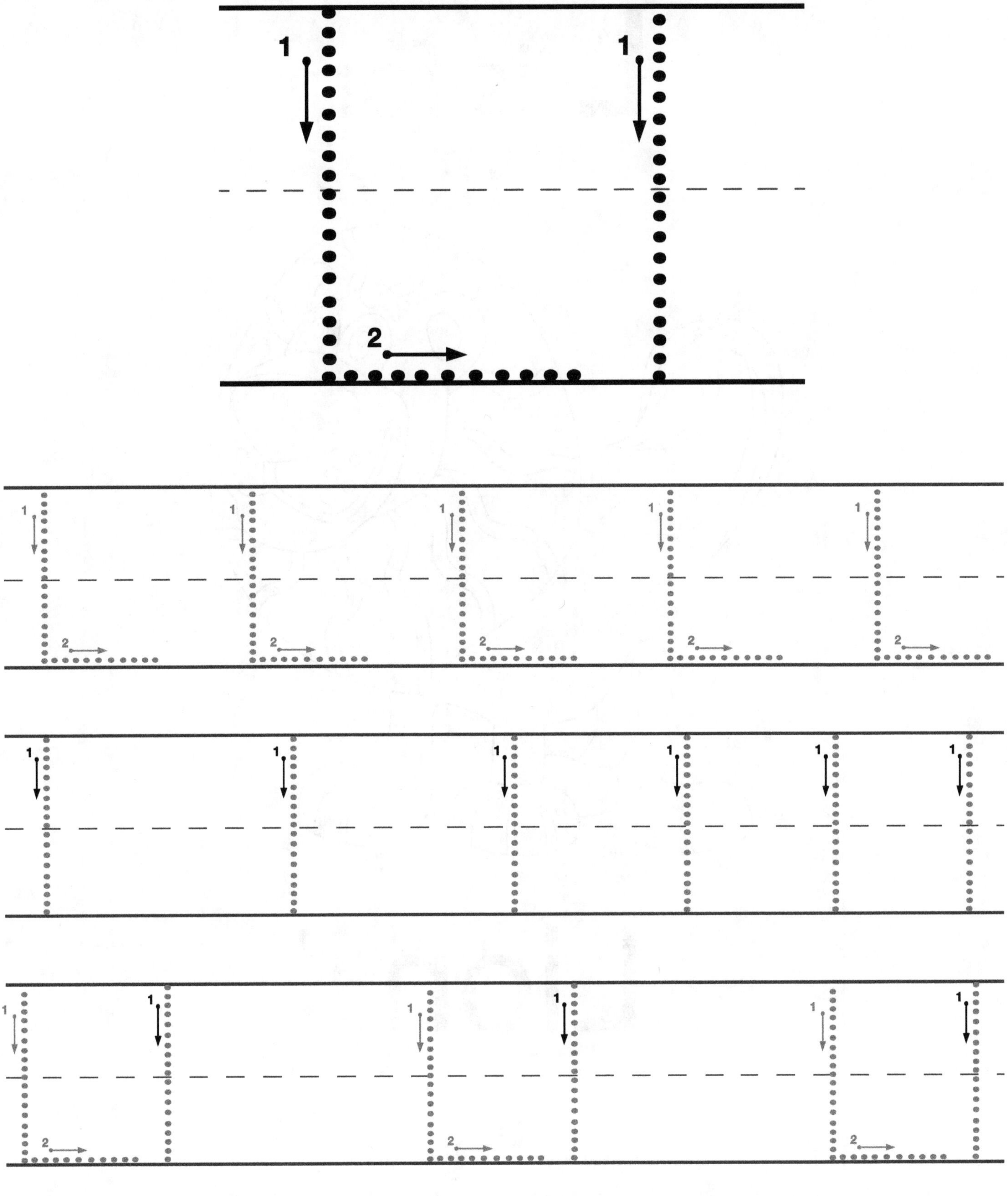

L is for

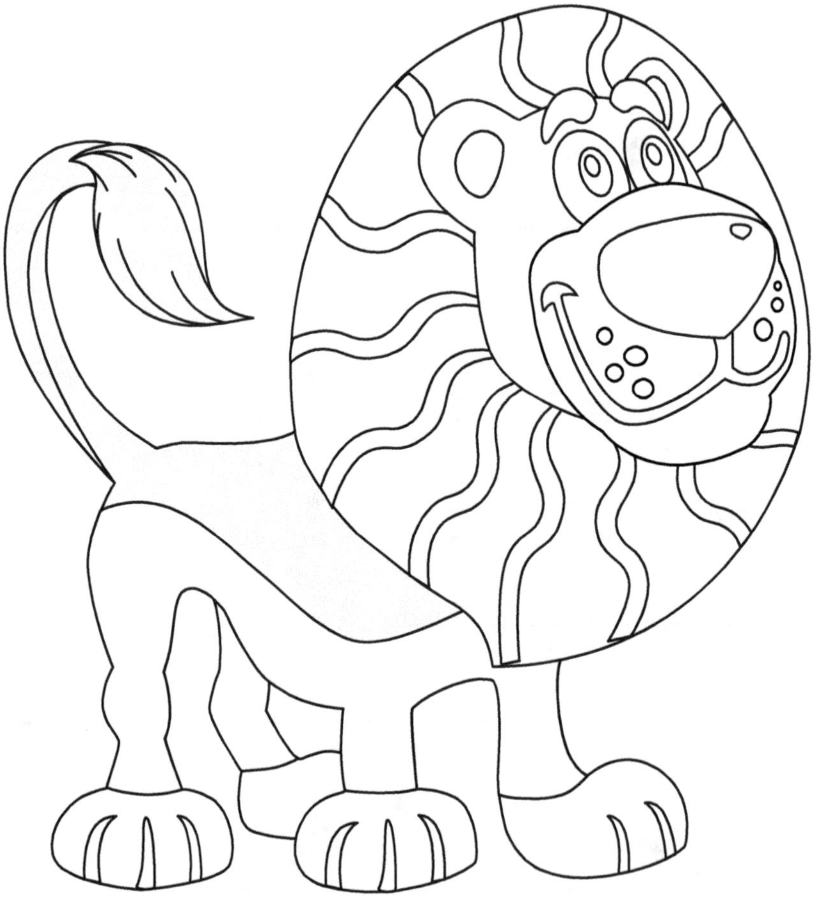

Lion

L

l

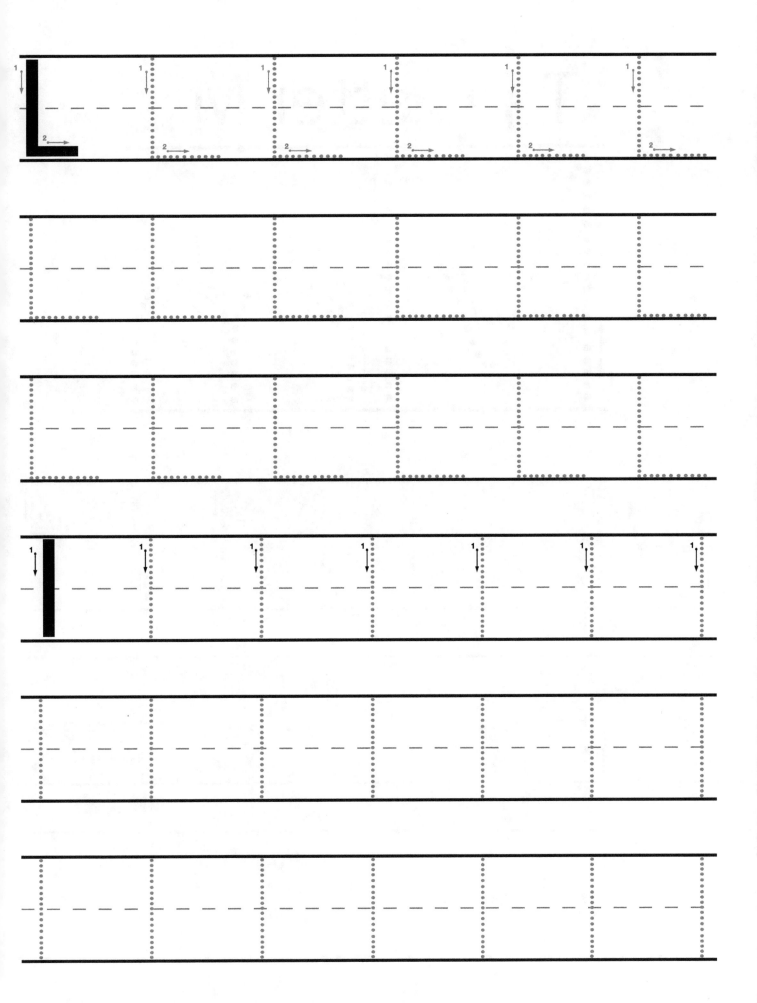

The Letter M

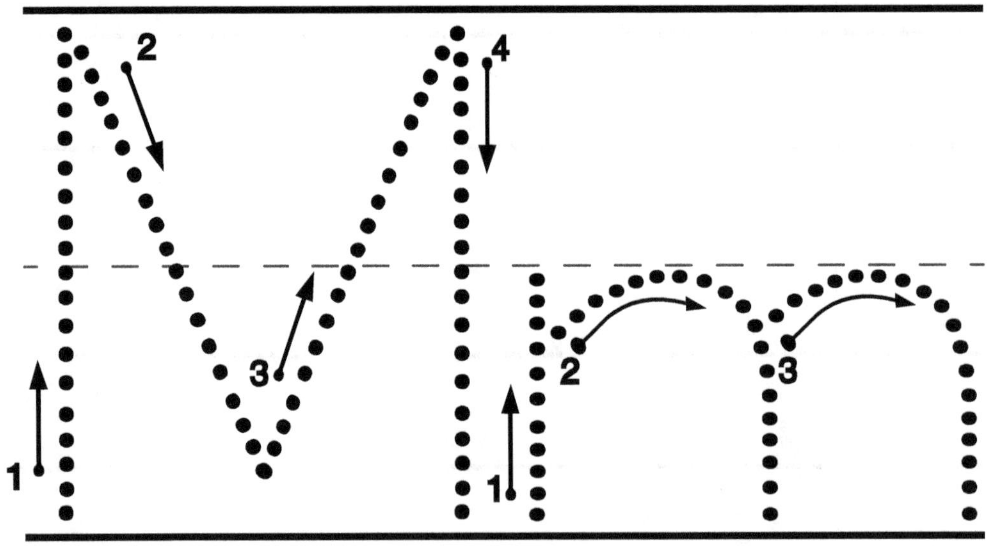

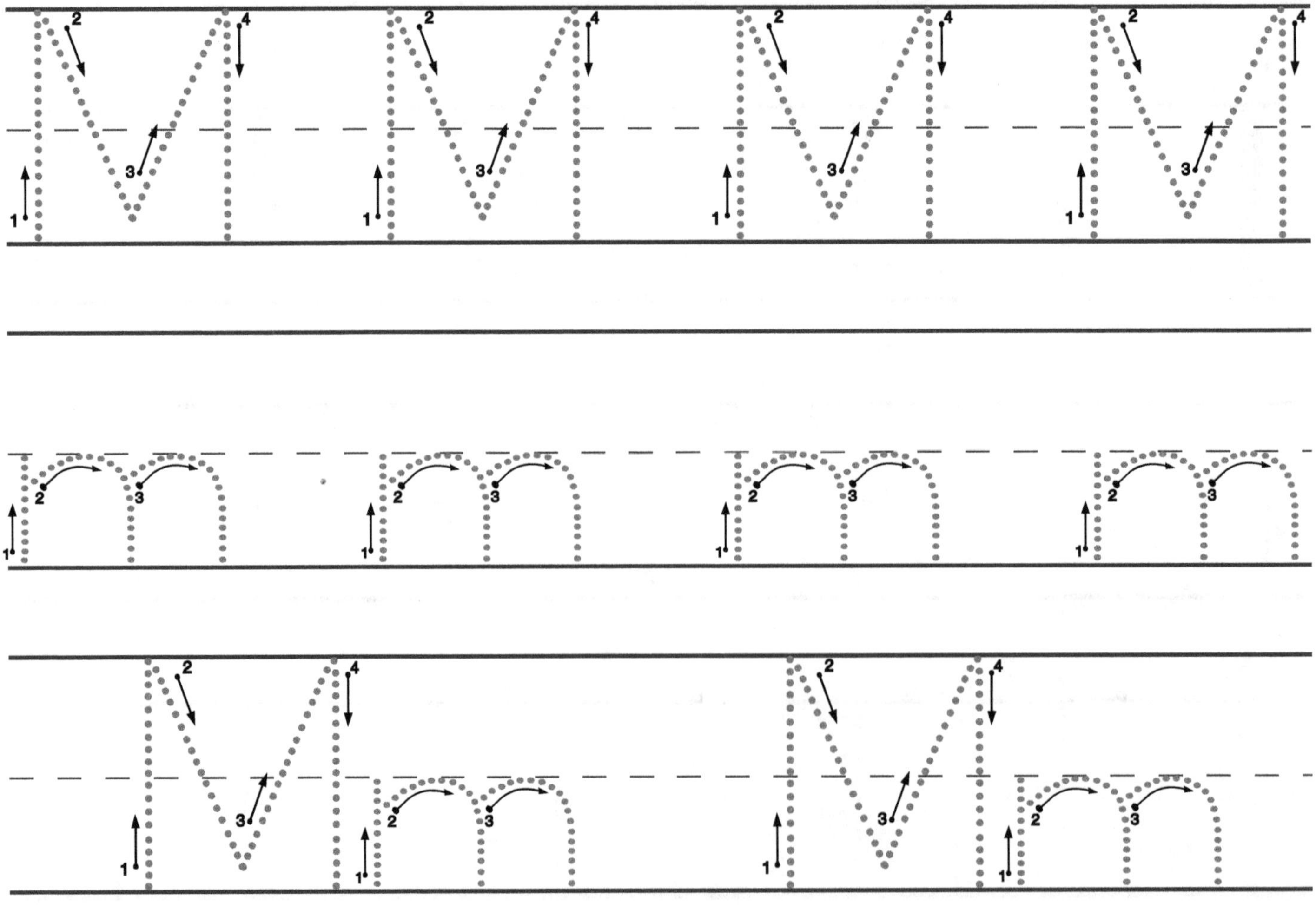

M is for

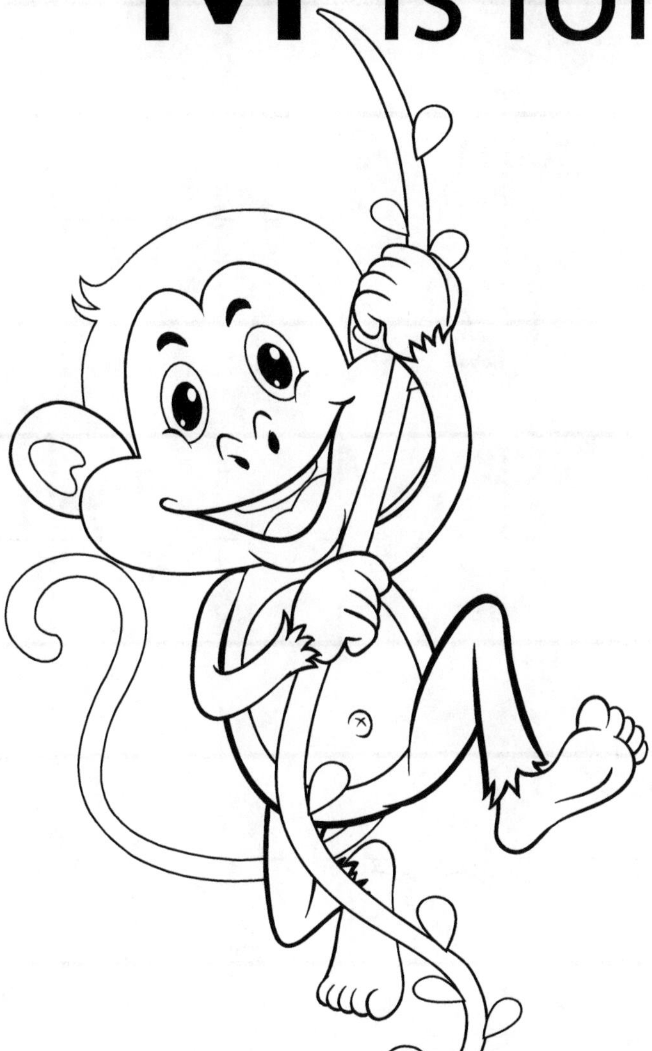

Monkey

M M M M M

M M M M M

M M M M M

m m m m m

m m m m m

m m m m m

The Letter N

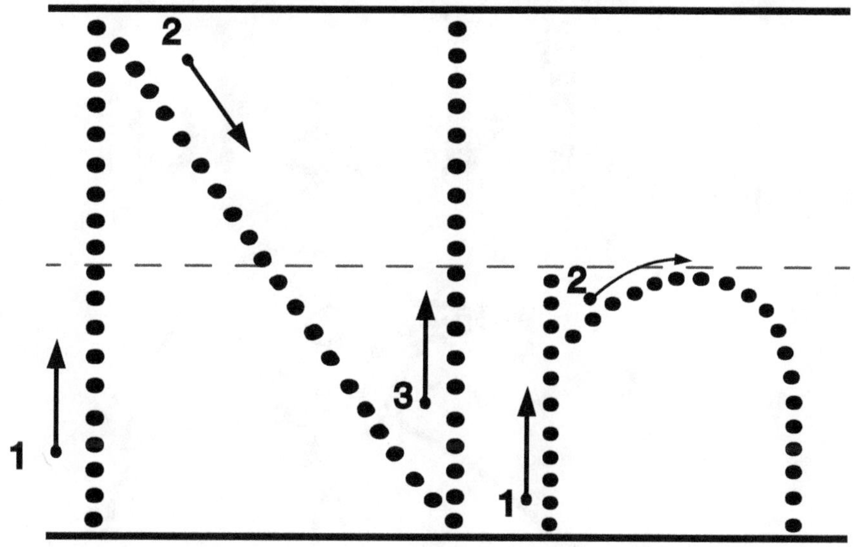

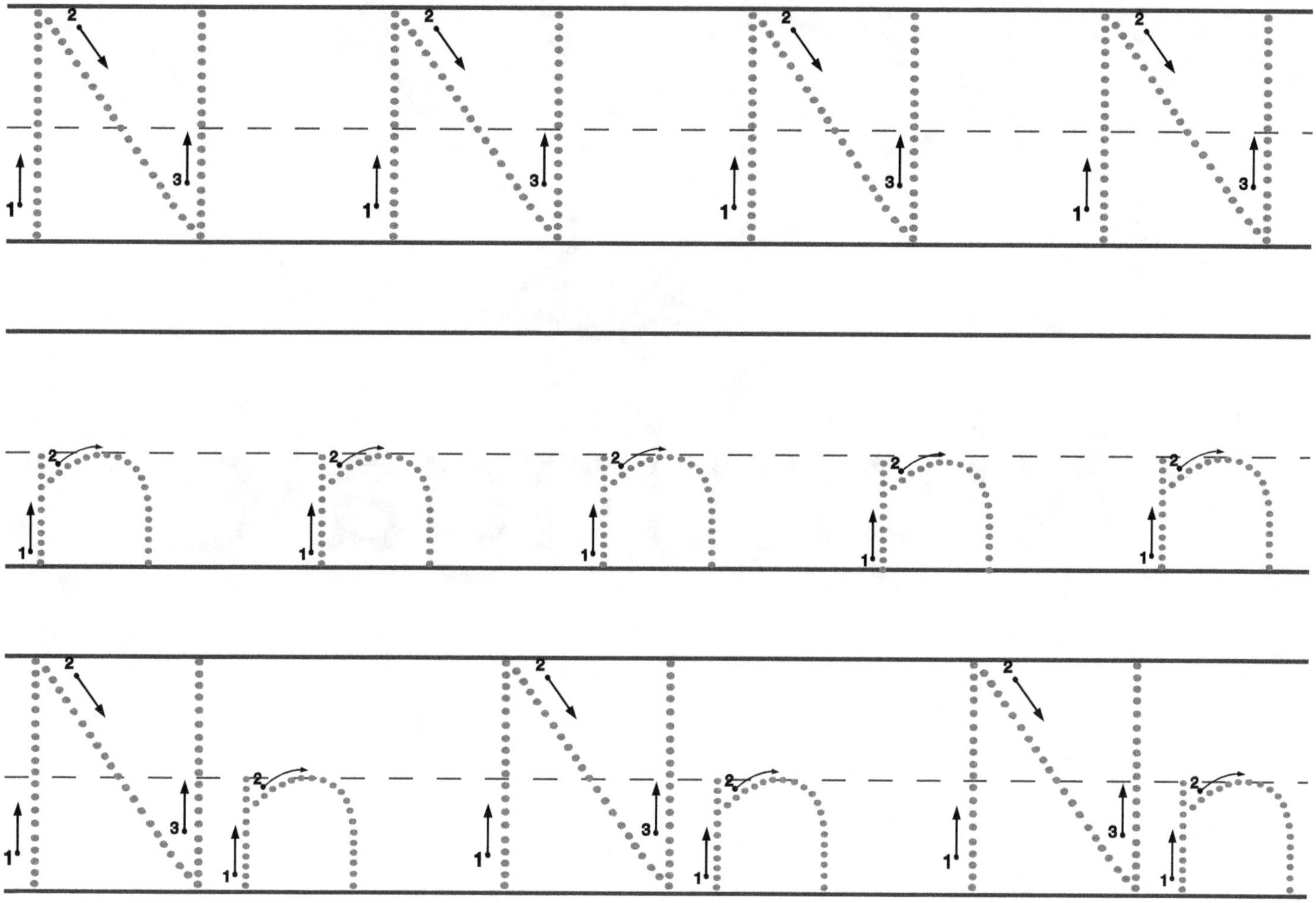

N is for

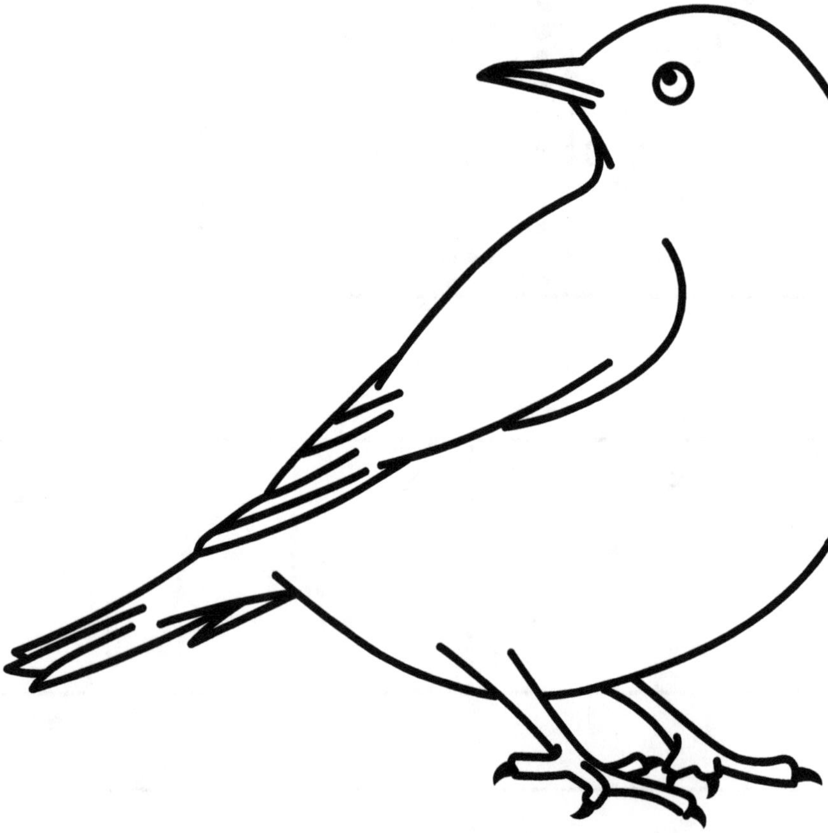

Nightingale

N N N N N

N N N N N

N N N N N

n n n n n n

n n n n n n

n n n n n n

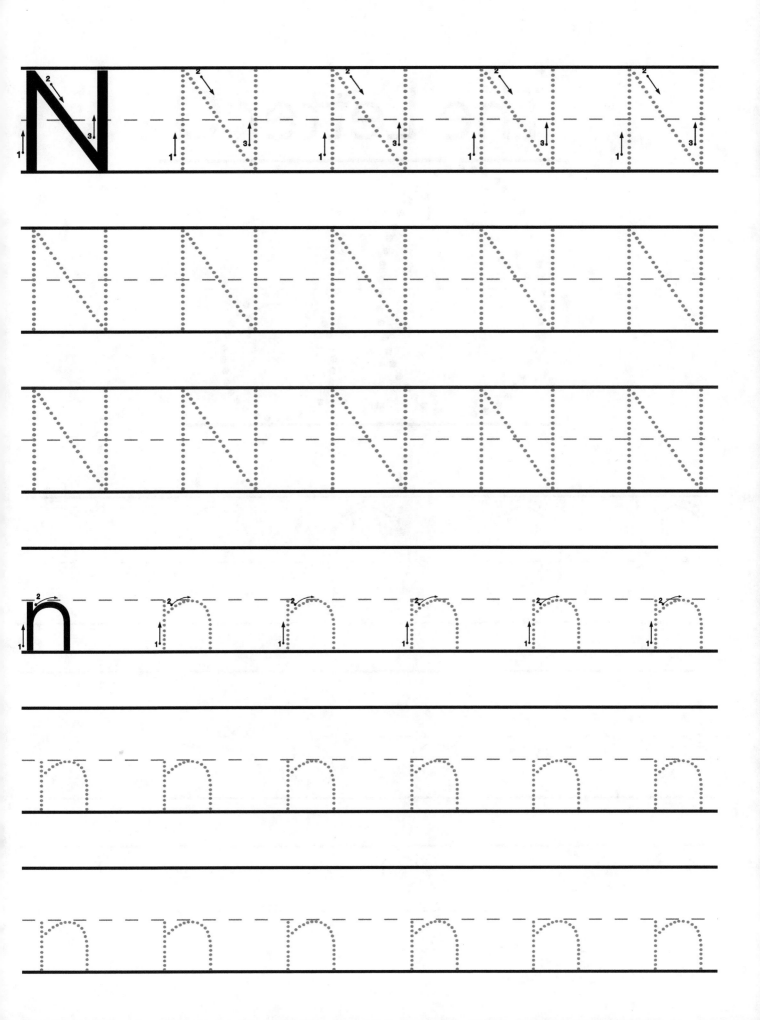

The Letter O

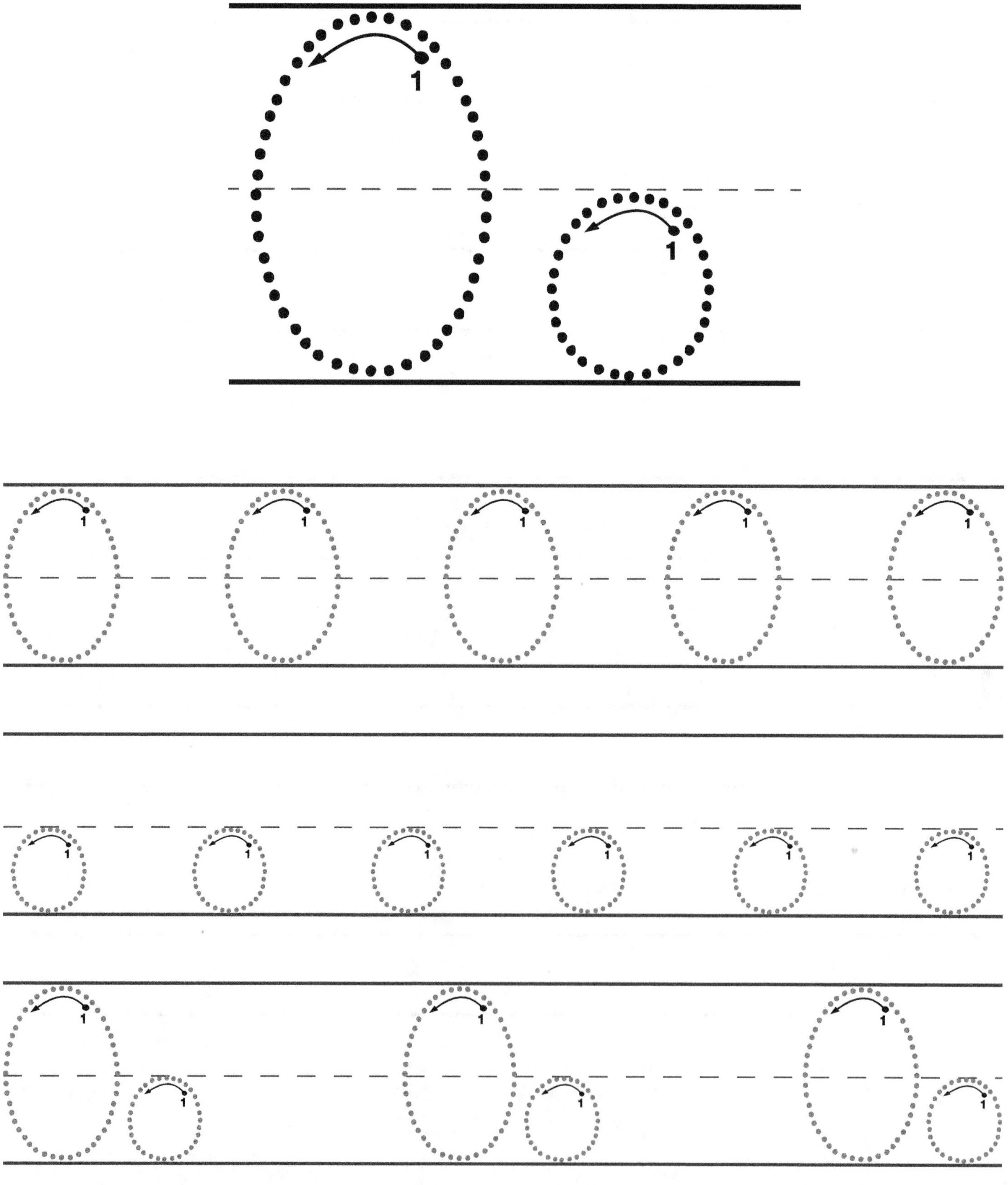

O is for

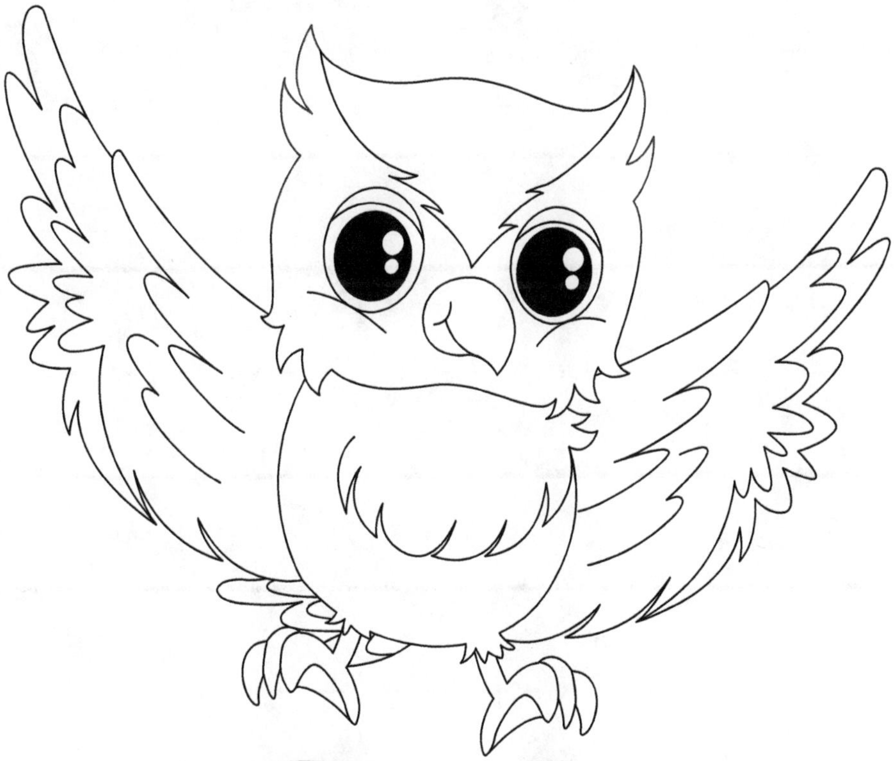

Owl

O 1

o 1

The Letter P

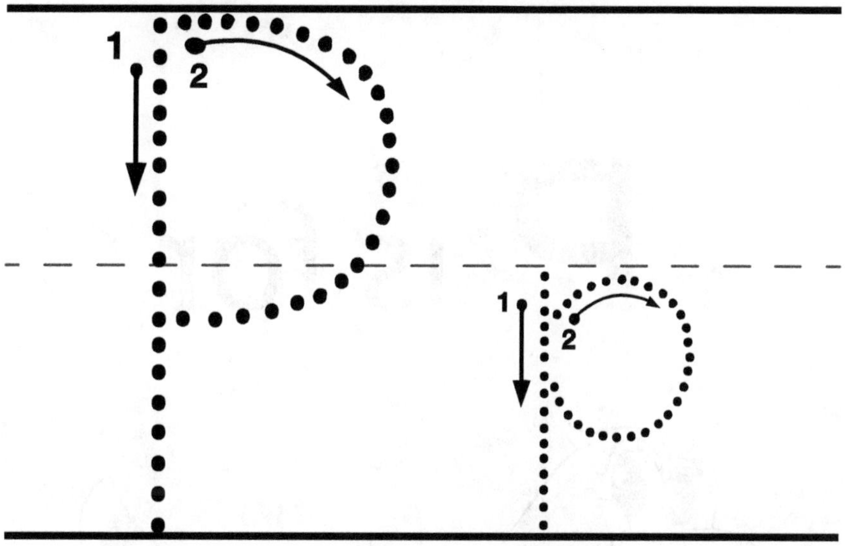

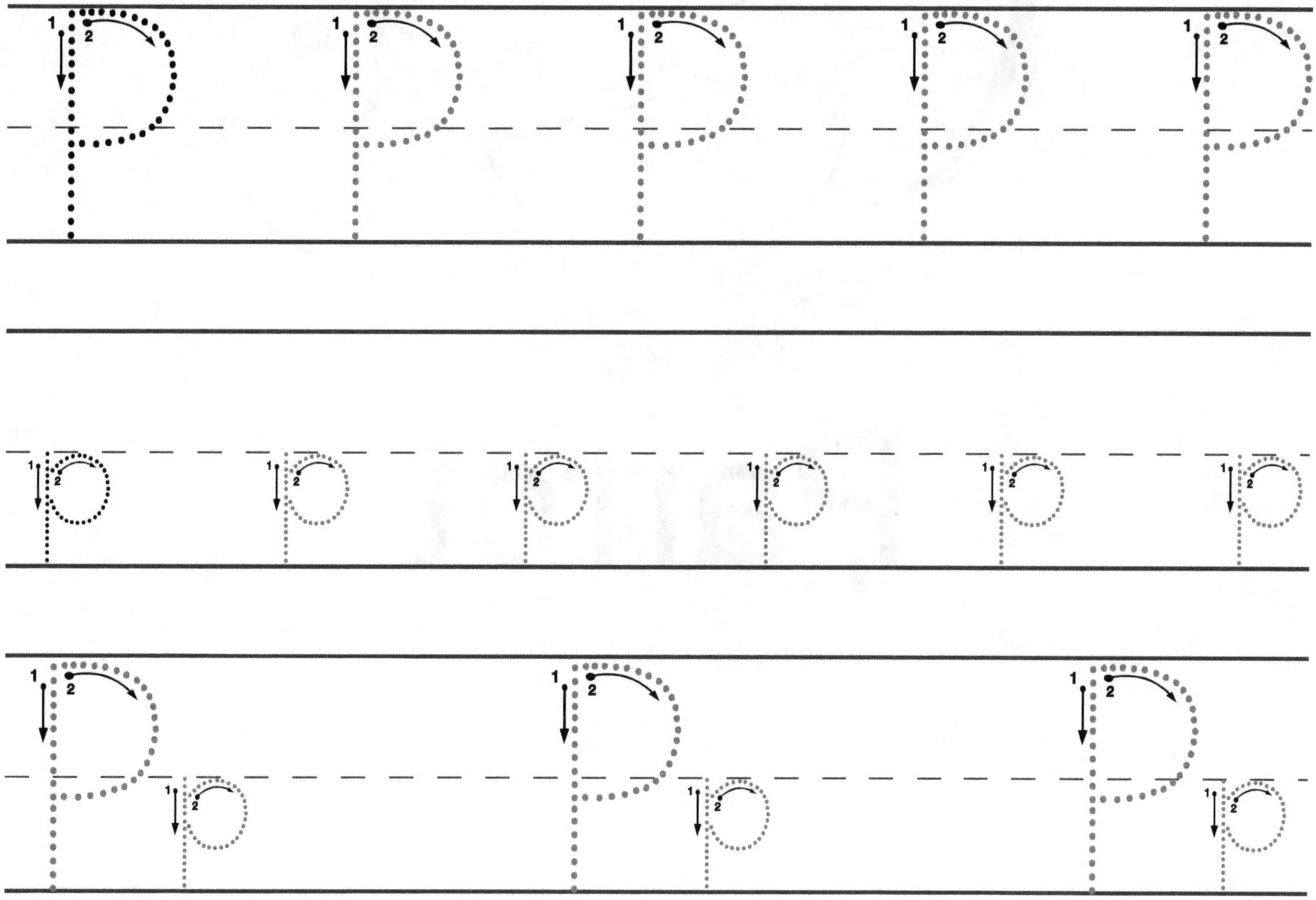

P is for

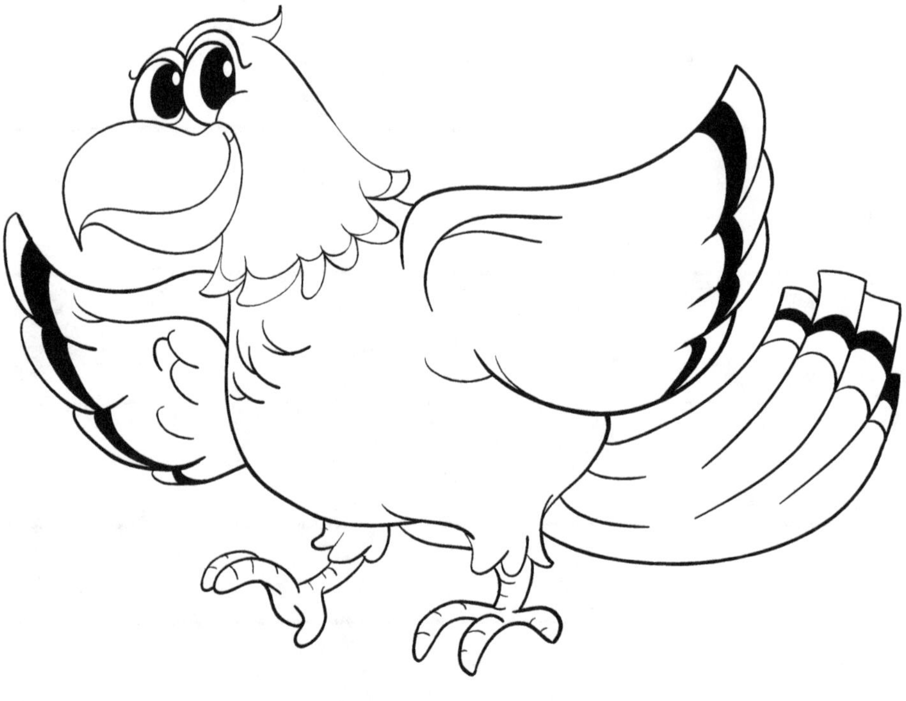

Parrot

1 P 2 — 1 2 P 1 2 P 1 2 P 1 2 P 1 2 P

P P P P P P

P P P P P P

1 p 2 — 1 2 p 1 2 p 1 2 p 1 2 p 1 2 p 1 2 p

p p p p p p p

p p p p p p p

The Letter Q

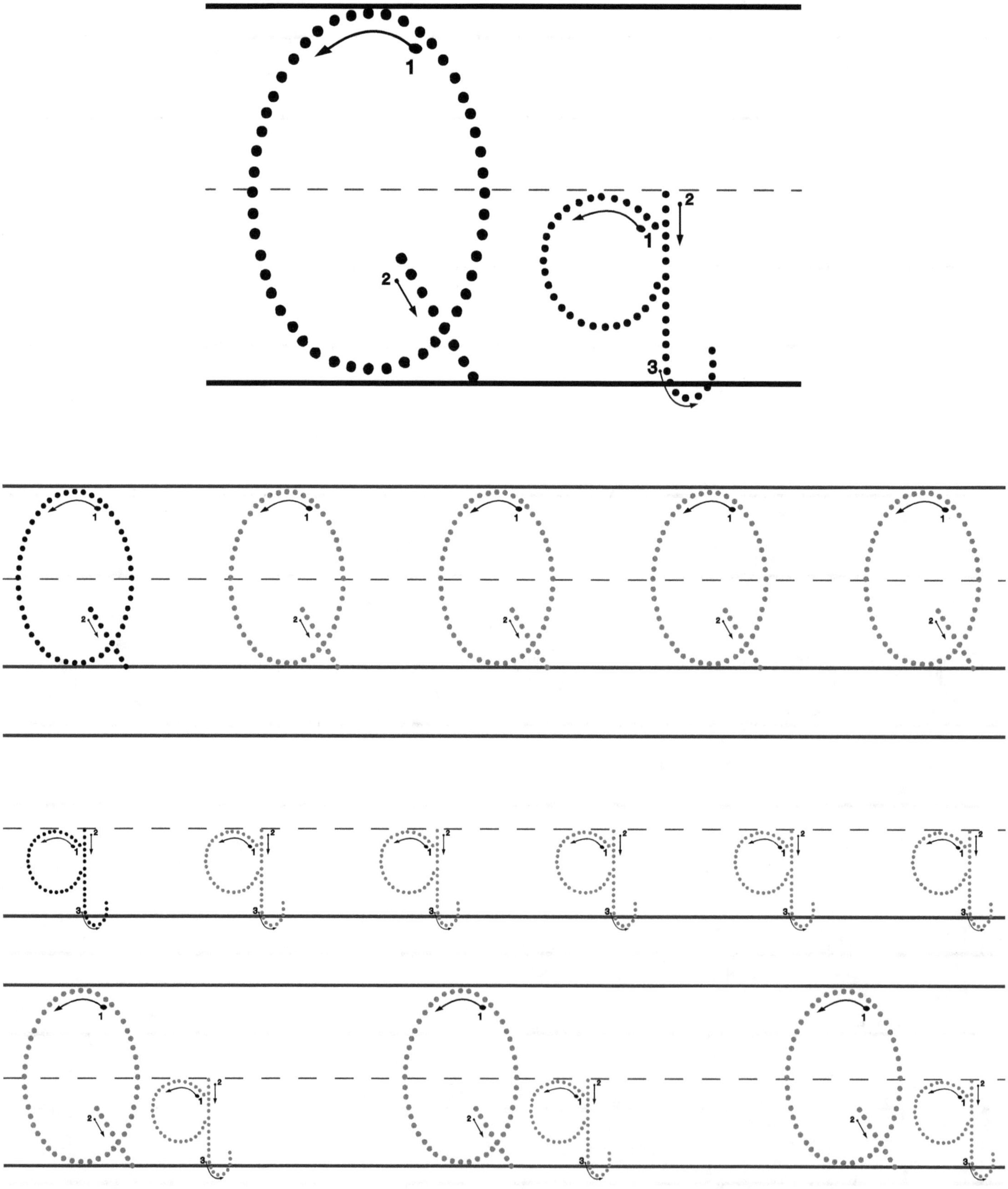

Q is for

Quack

Q

Q Q Q Q Q

Q Q Q Q Q Q

Q Q Q Q Q Q

q q q q q q q

q q q q q q q

q q q q q q q

The Letter R

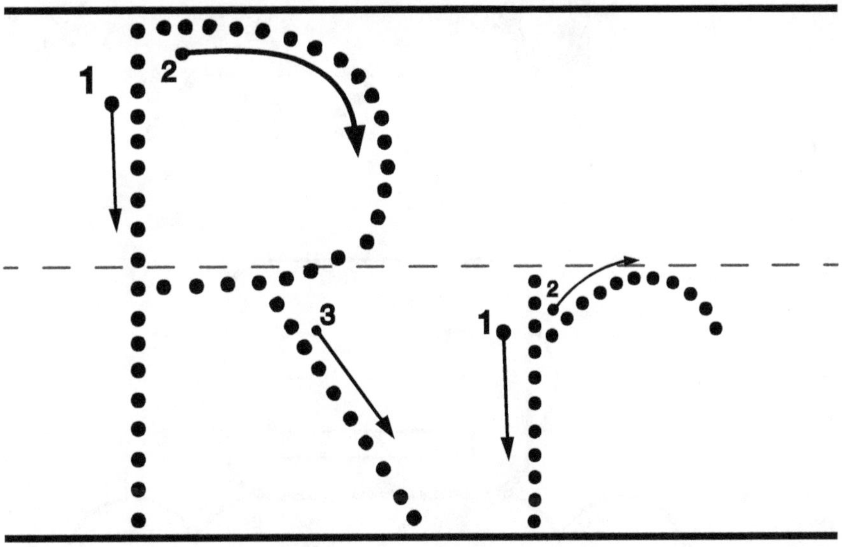

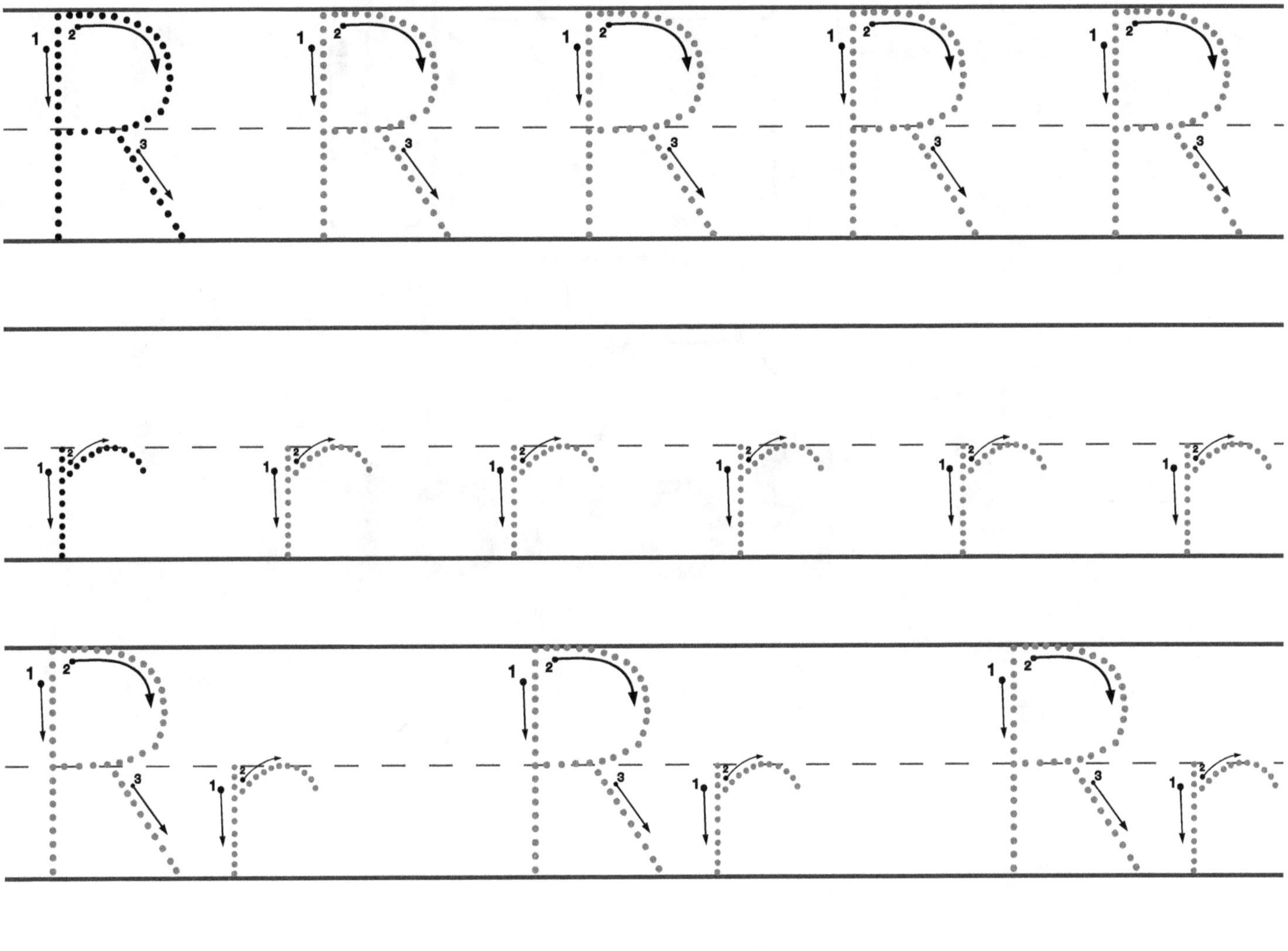

R is for

Robot

R R R R R R

R R R R R R

R R R R R R

r r r r r r

r r r r r r

r r r r r r

The Letter **S**

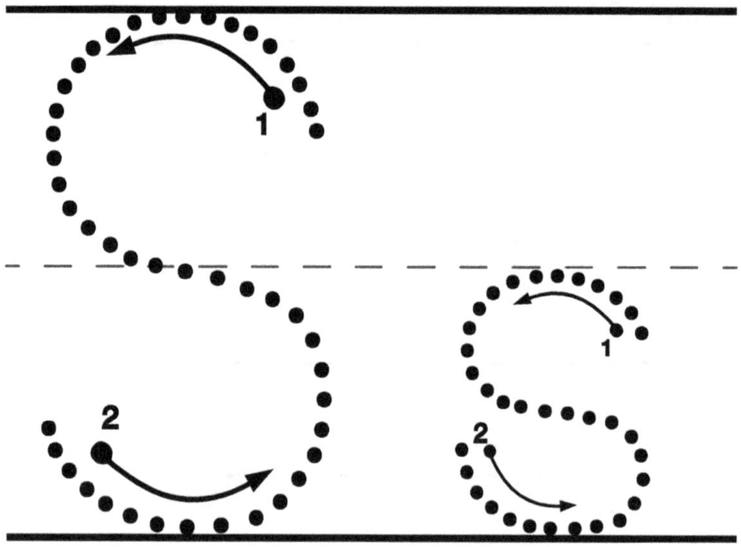

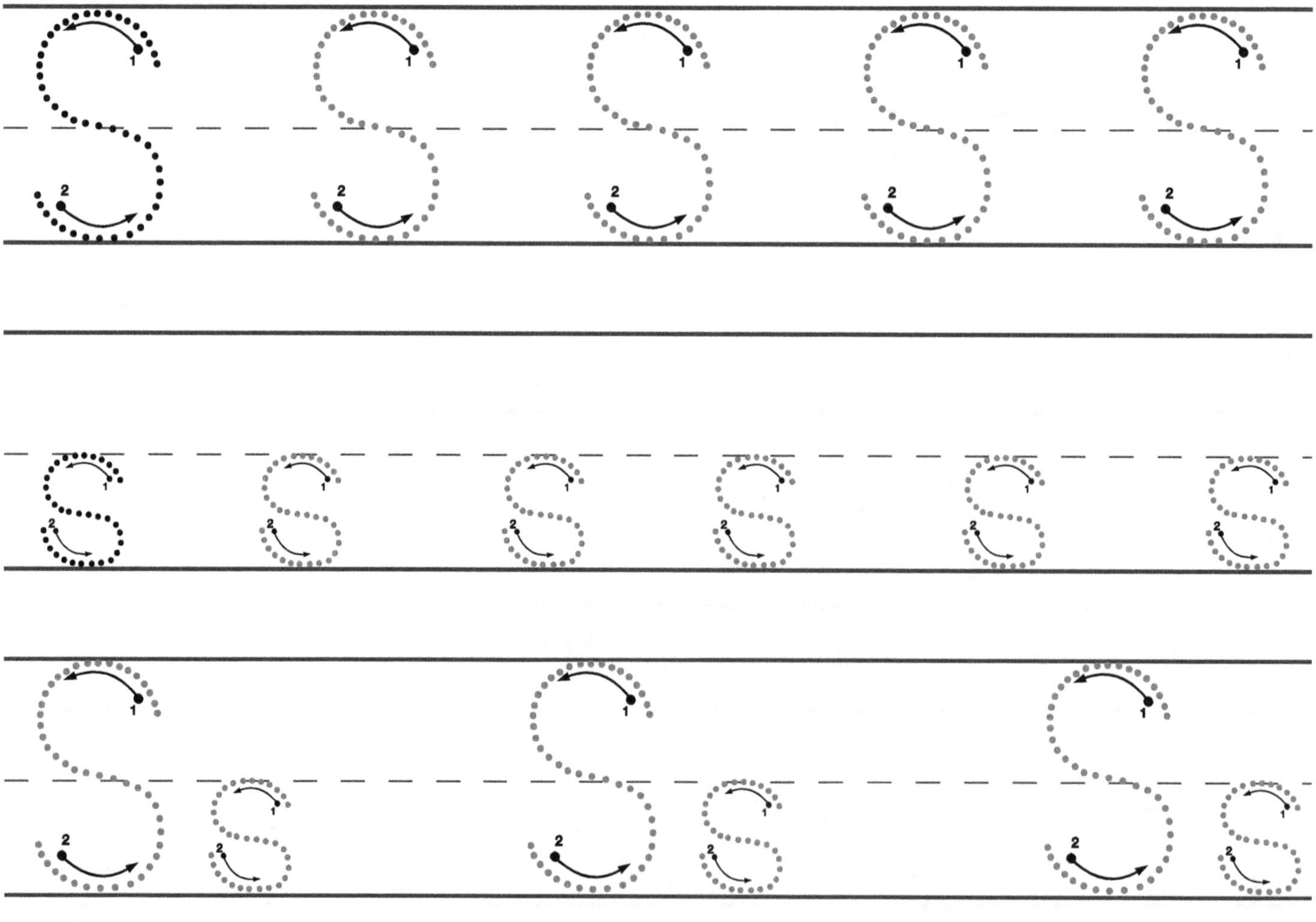

S

s

The Letter T

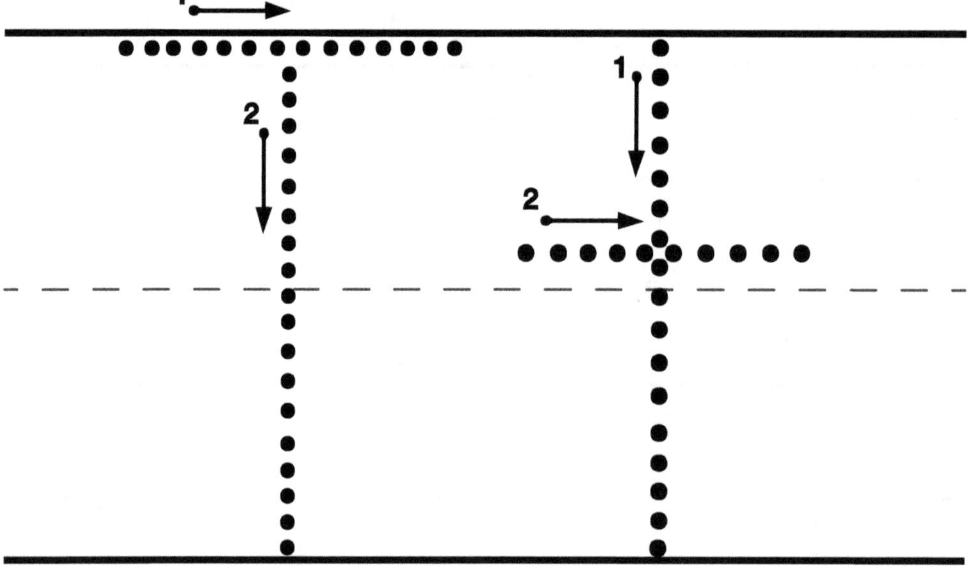

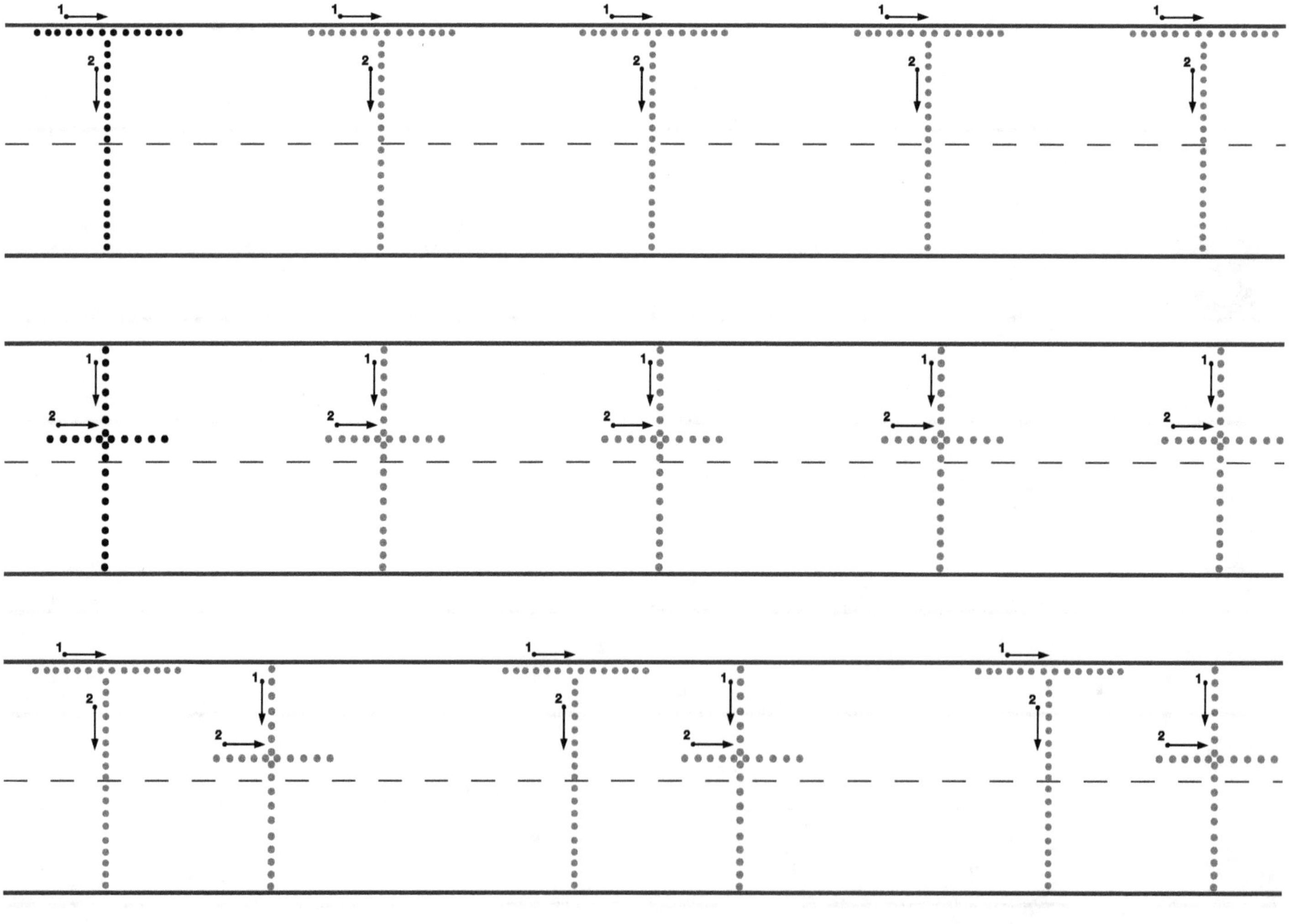

T is for

Turtle

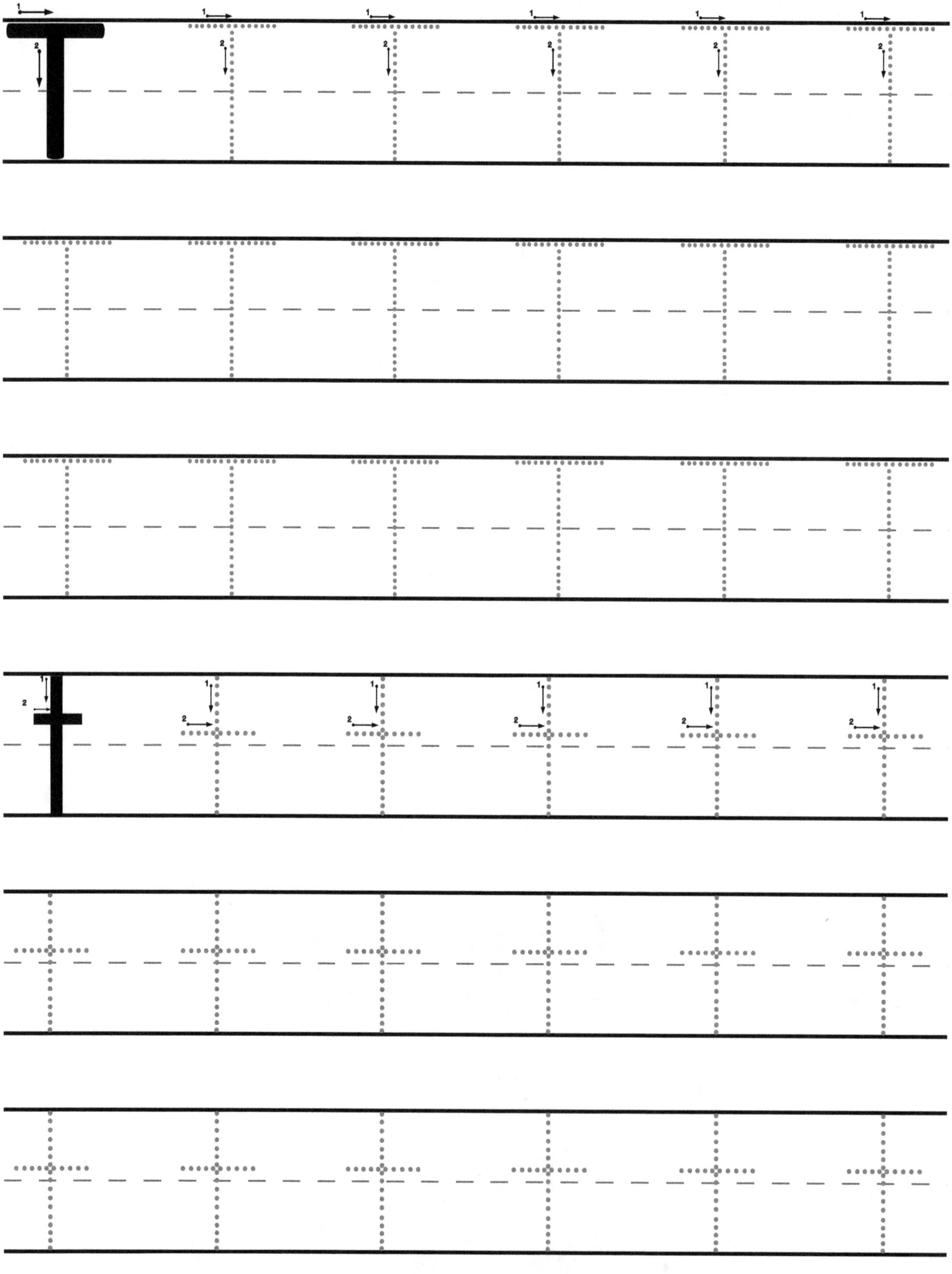

The Letter u

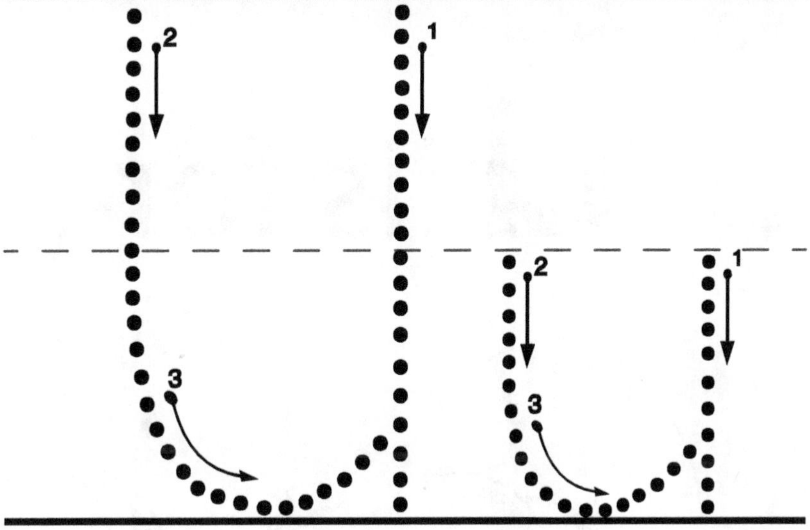

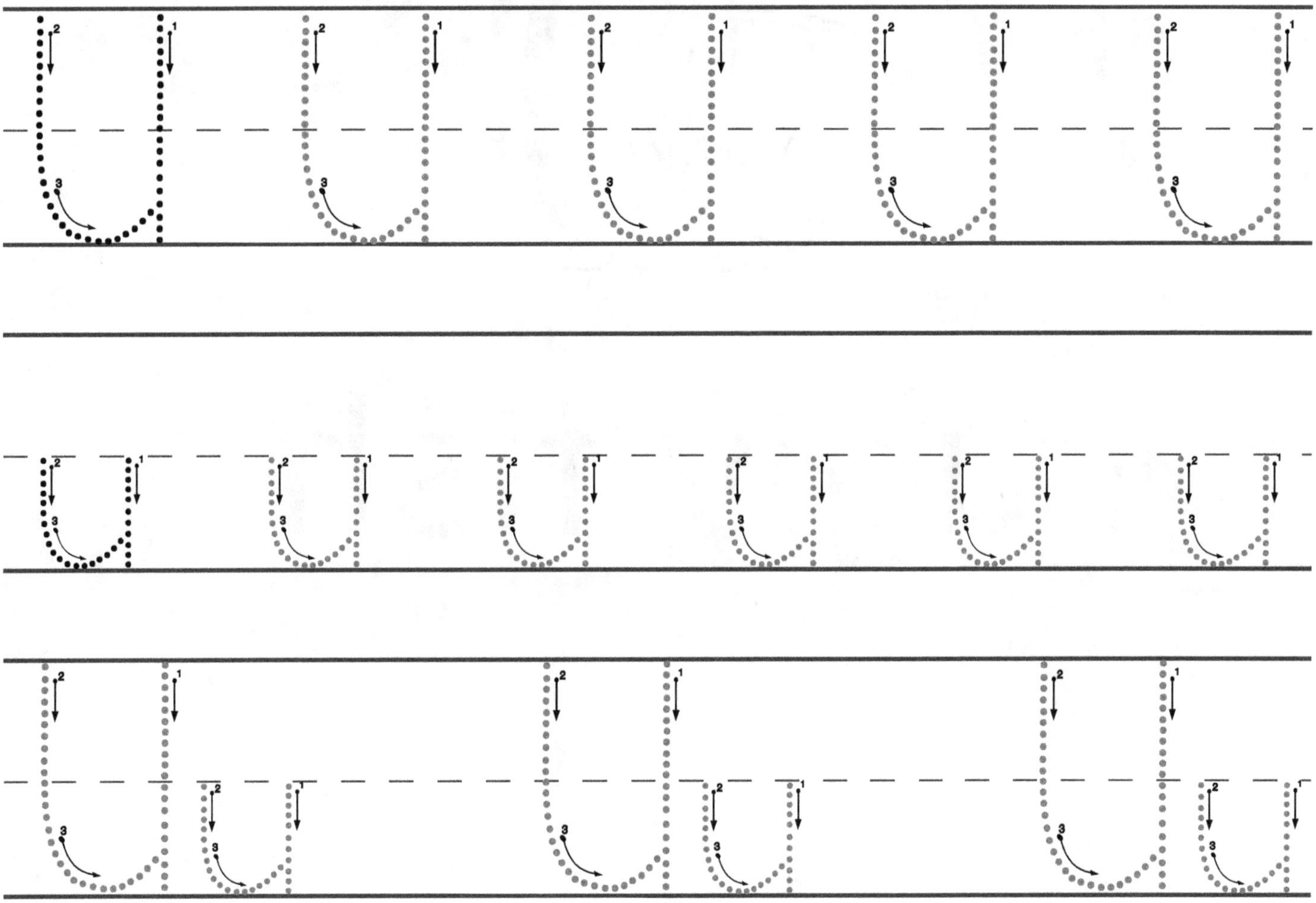

u is for

ugly fish

u u u u u u

u u u u u u

u u u u u u

u u u u u u u u

u u u u u u u u

u u u u u u u u

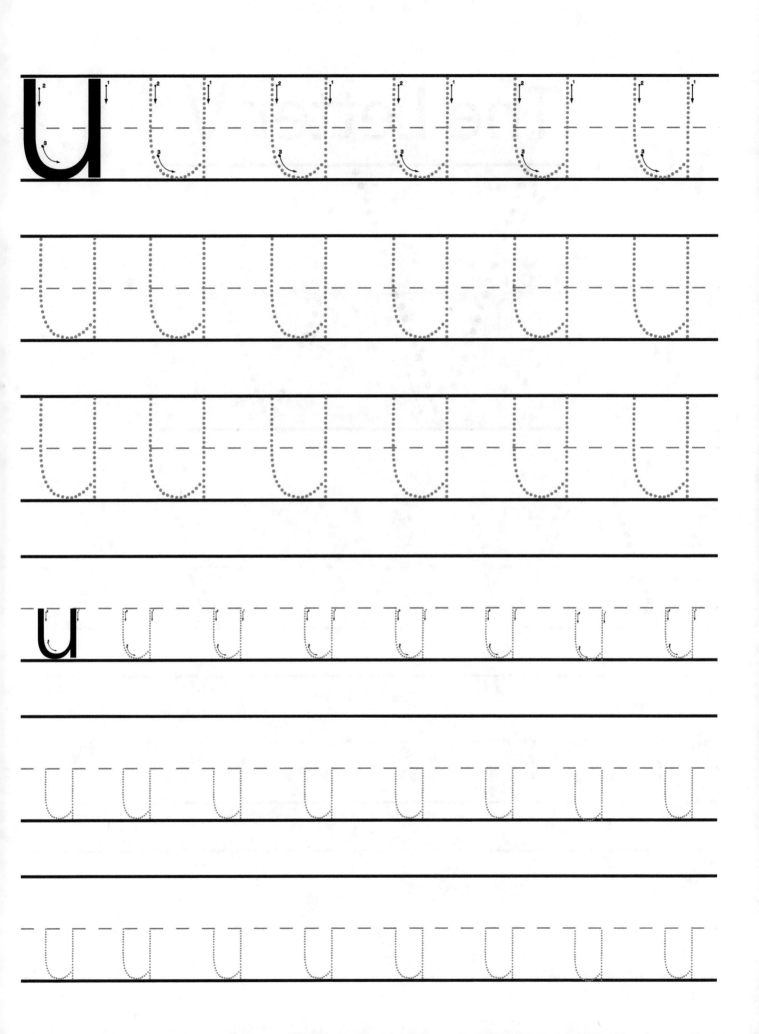

The Letter V

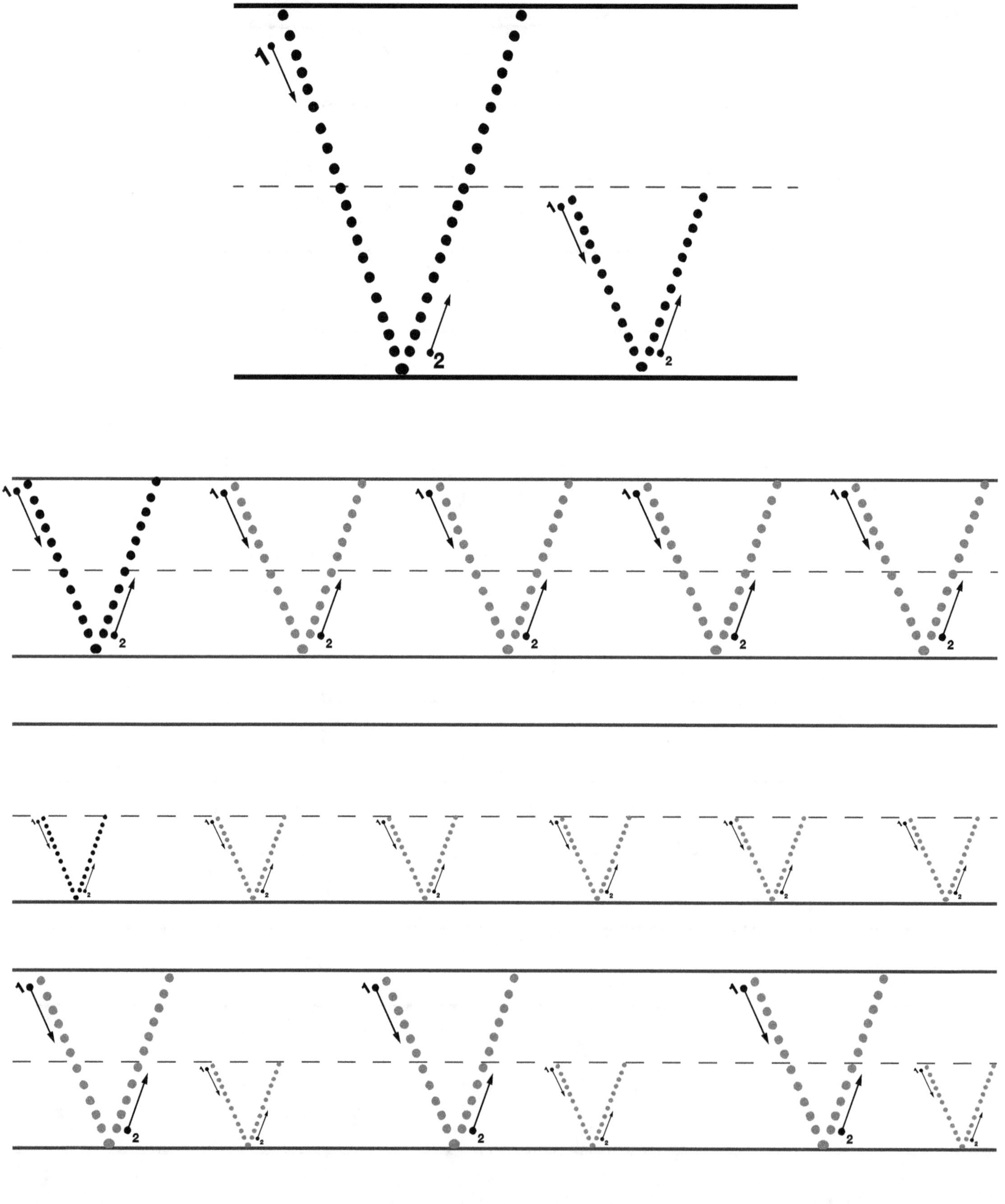

V V V V V

V V V V V

V V V V V

v v v v v v v

v v v v v v v

v v v v v v v

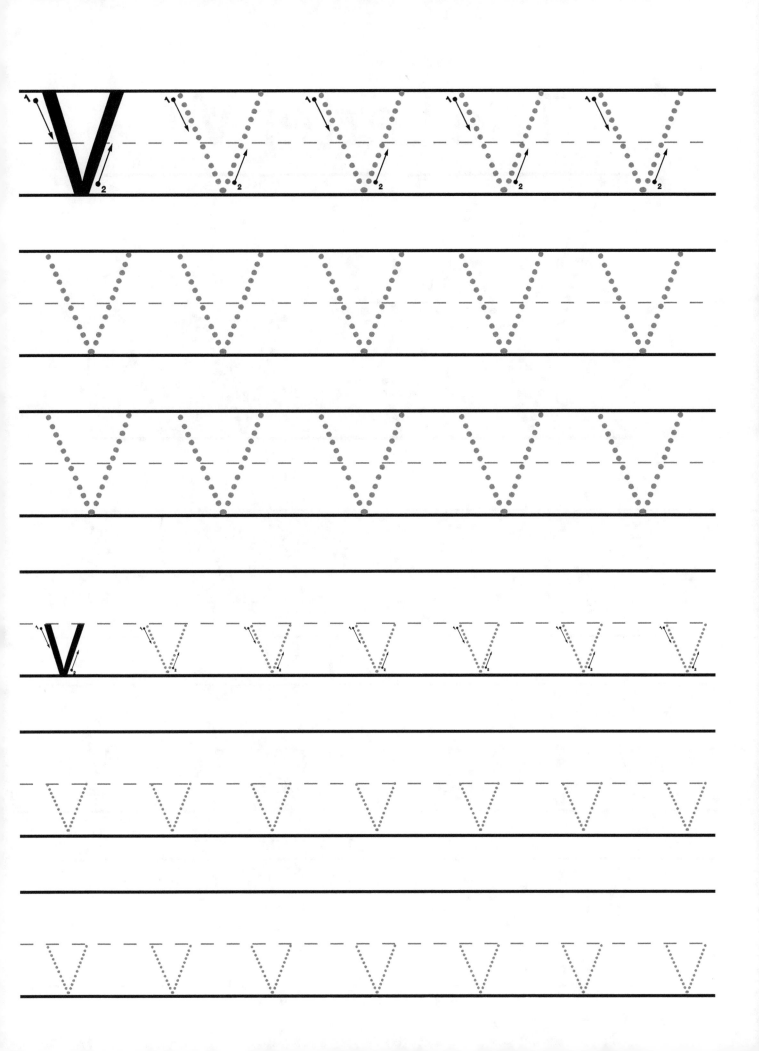

The Letter W

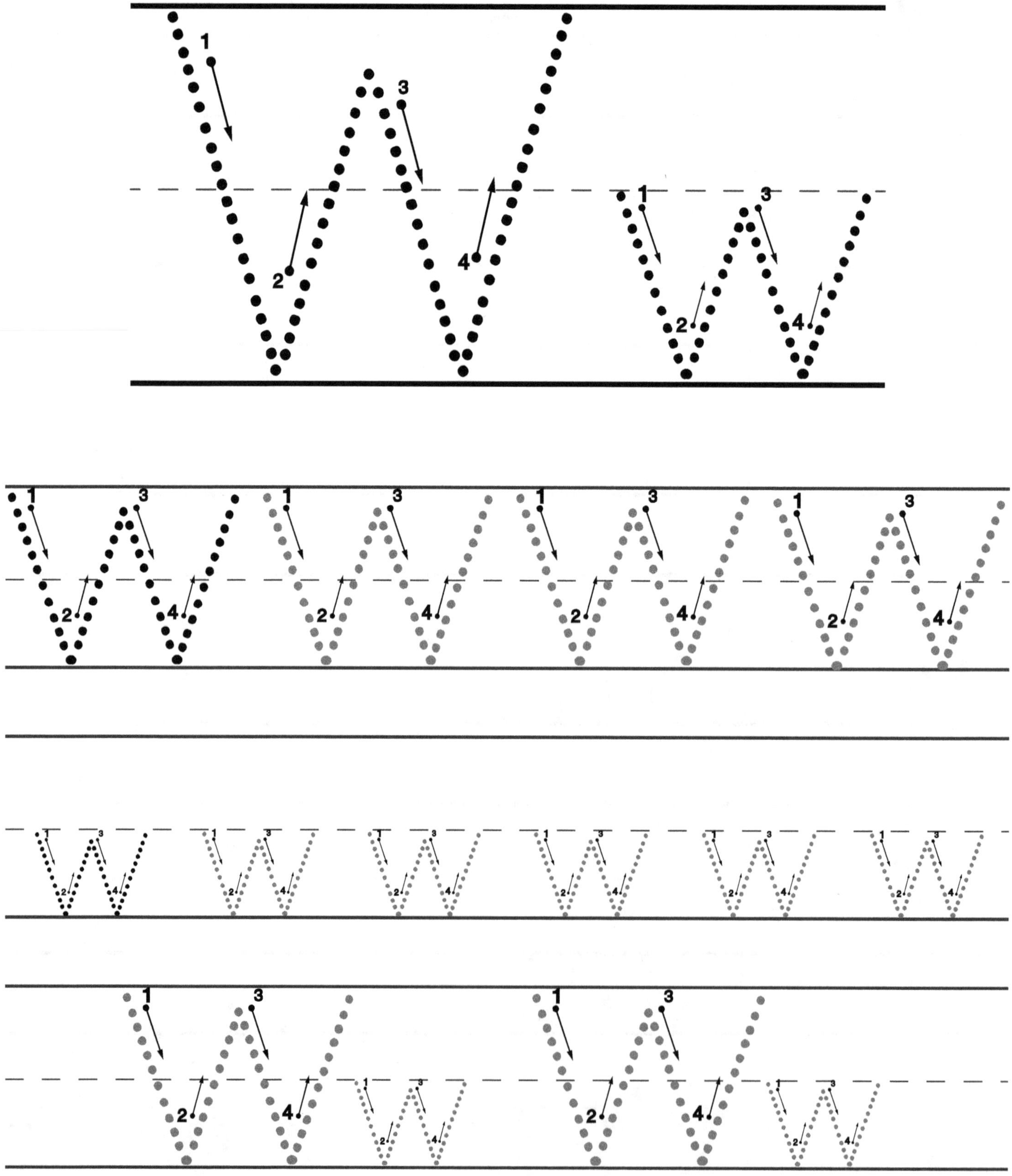

W is for

Walrus

W W W W

W W W W

W W W W

w w w w w w

w w w w w w

w w w w w w

The Letter X

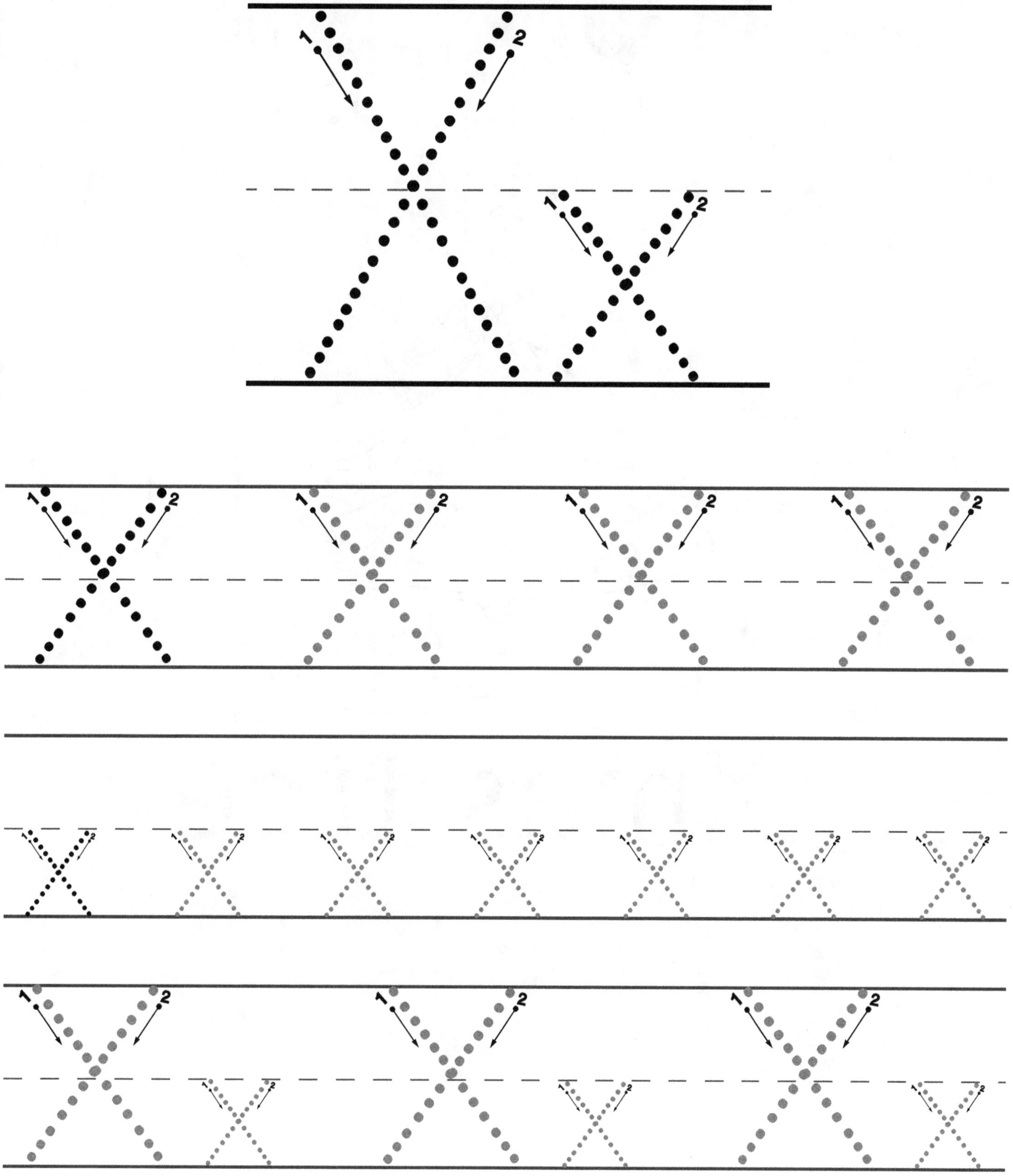

X is for

Xmas tree

1 X 2   1 X 2   1 X 2   1 X 2   1 X 2

X X X X X

X X X X X

1 X 2   1 X 2   1 X 2   1 X 2   1 X 2   1 X 2   1 X 2   1 X 2

X X X X X X X X

X X X X X X X X

The Letter Y

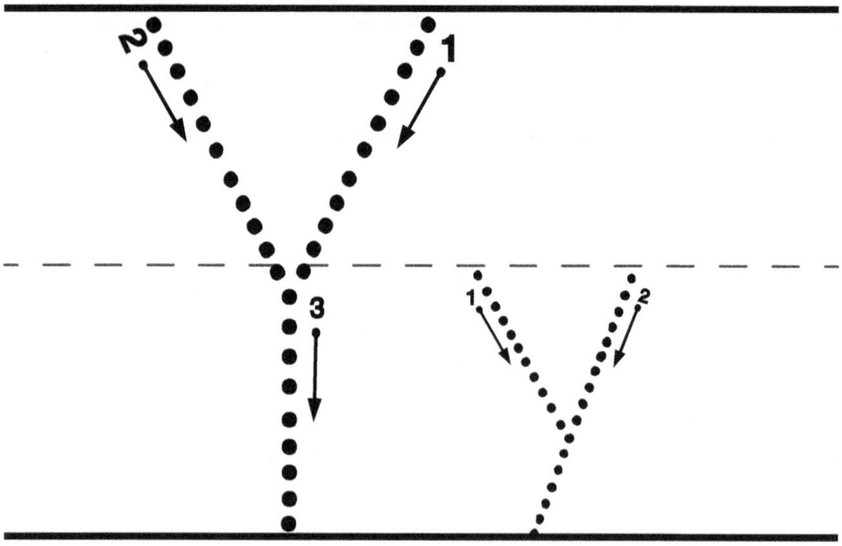

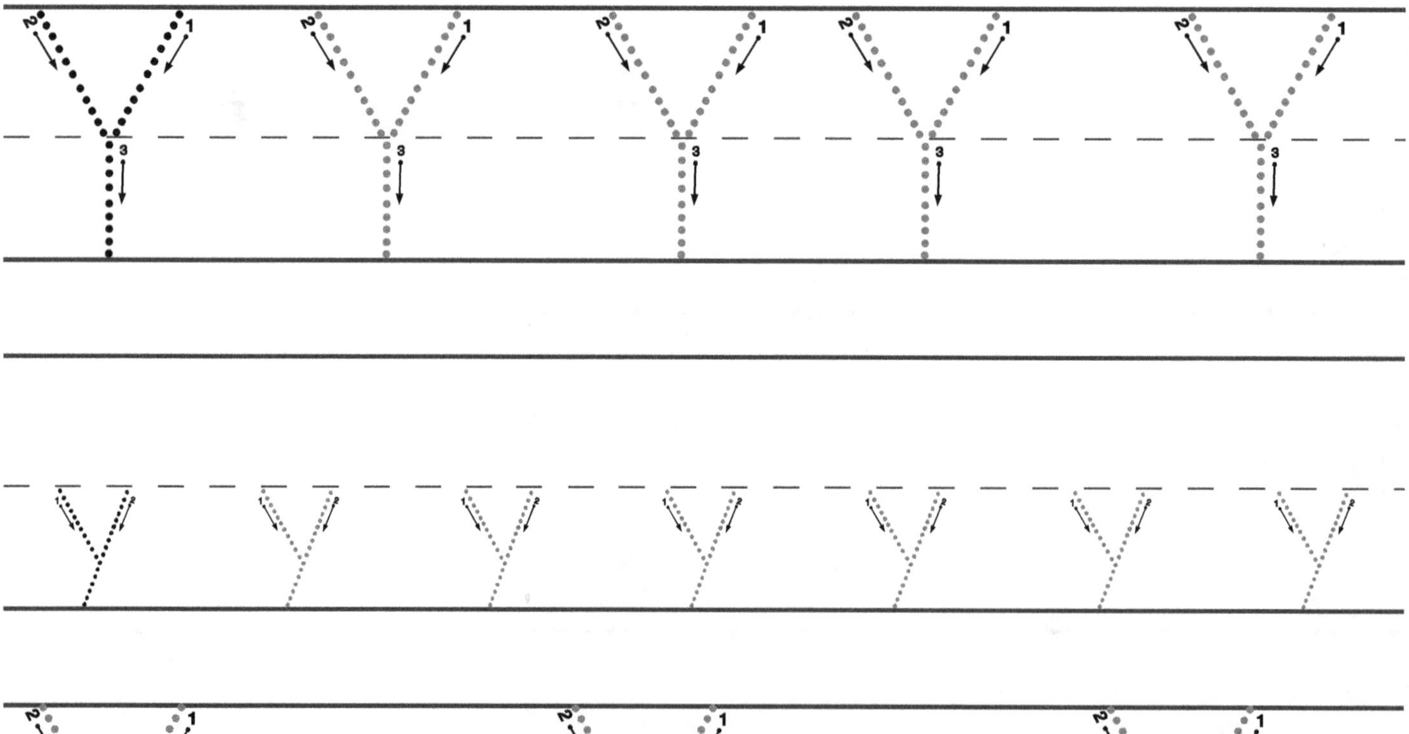

Y is for

Yacht

Y

y

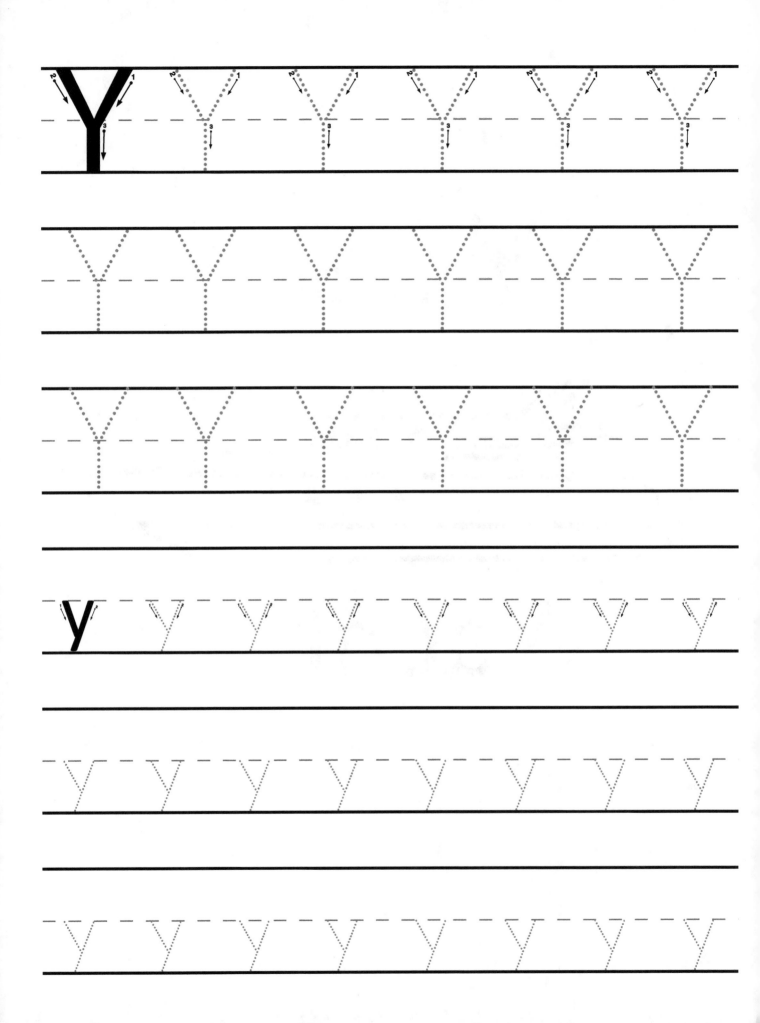

The Letter Z

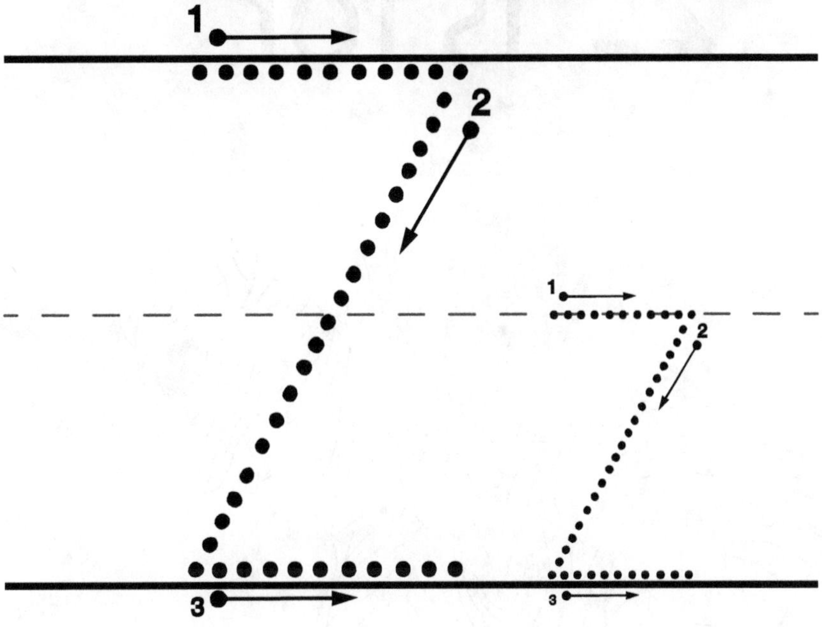

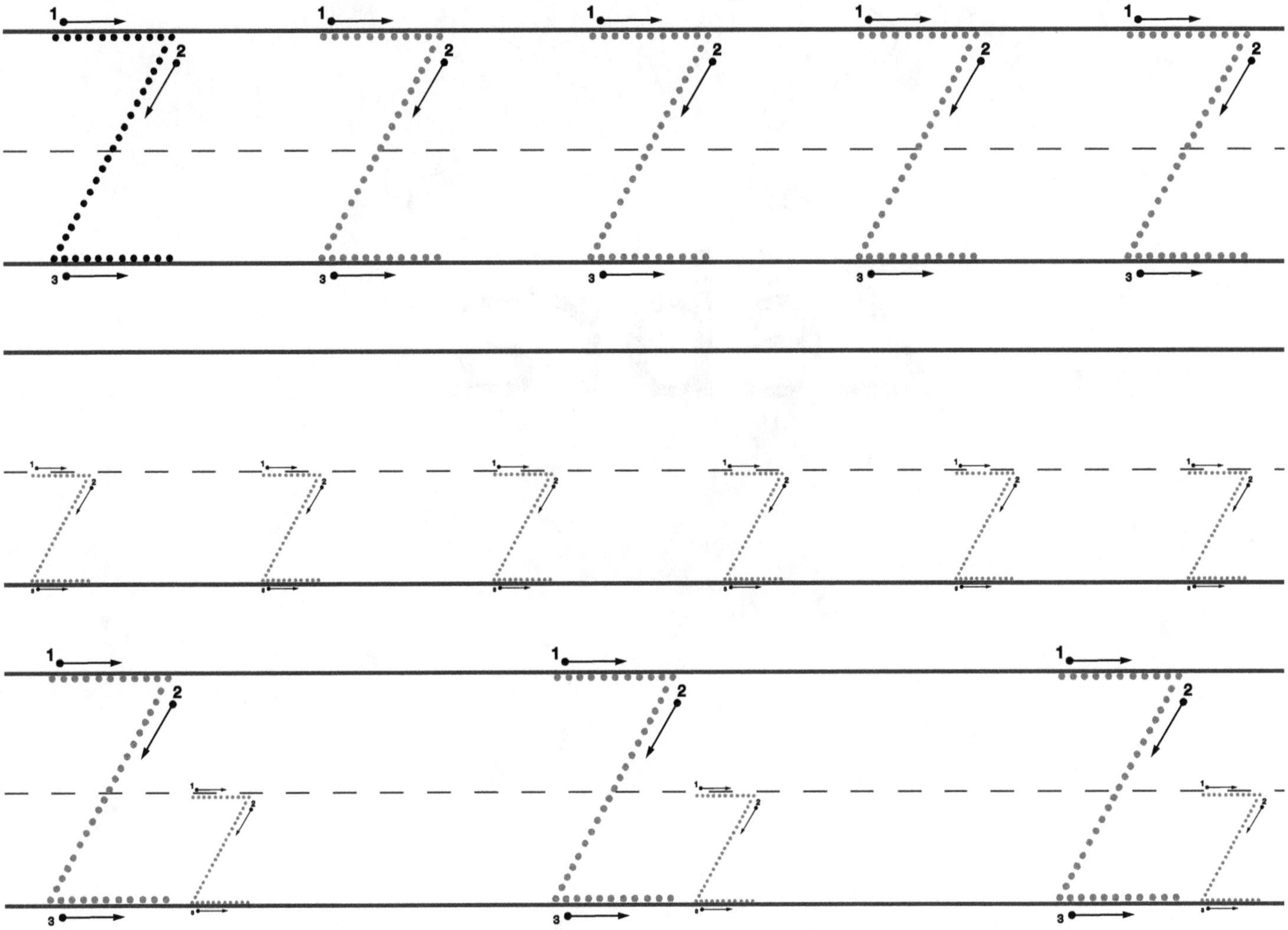

Z is for

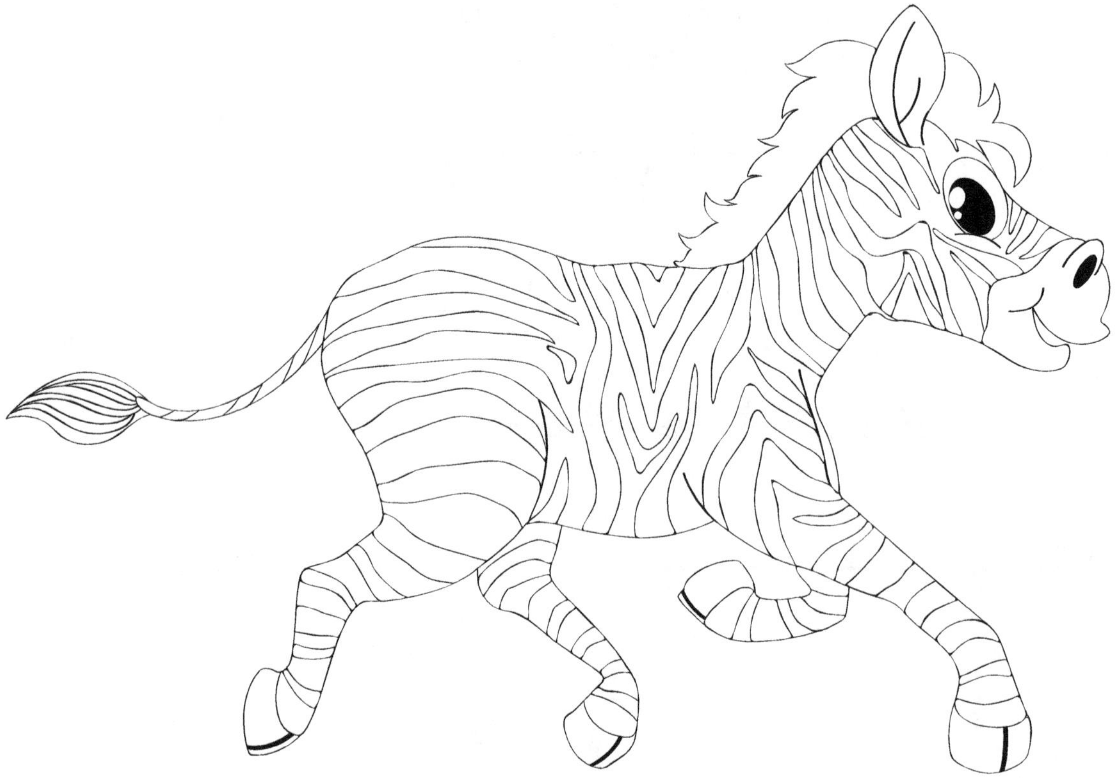

Zebra

Z

z

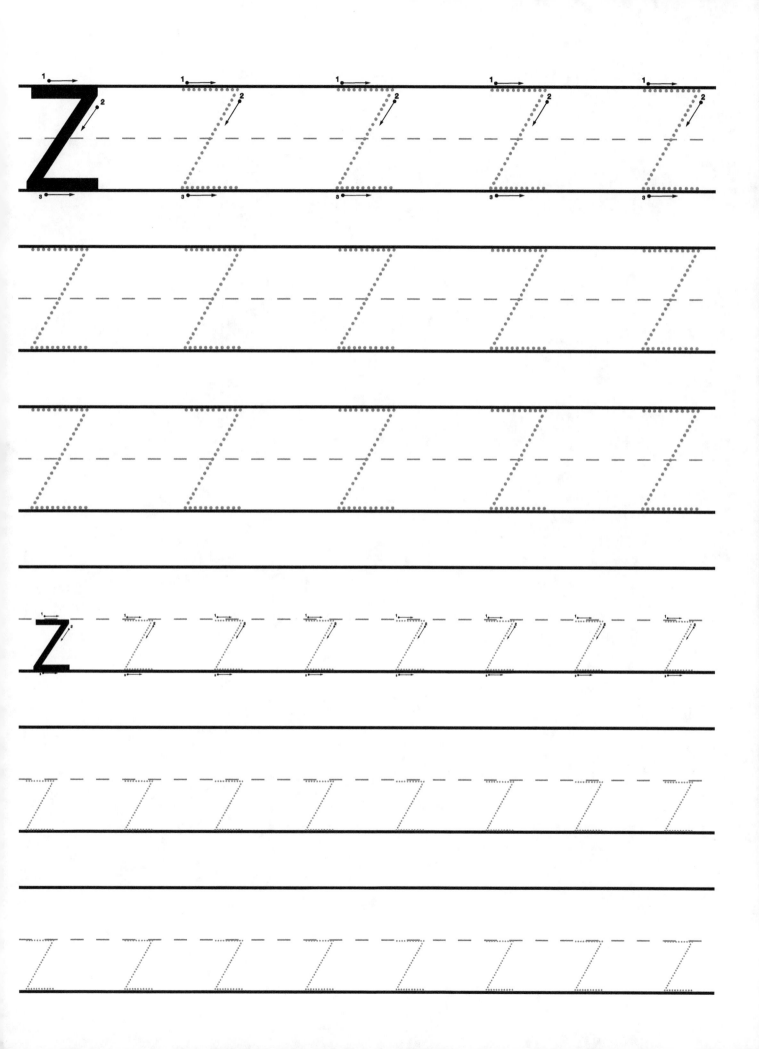

All graphic use in this book from:

www.vecteezy.com

Printed in the USA
CPSIA information can be obtained
at www.ICGtesting.com
LVHW070438100124
768593LV00044BA/1340

9 798644 621064